INSECTS AND MITES ASSOCIATED WITH ONTARIO FORESTS:

CLASSIFICATION, COMMON NAMES, MAIN HOSTS AND IMPORTANCE

P.D. SYME and K.L. NYSTROM

GREAT LAKES FORESTRY CENTRE

SAULT STE. MARIE, ONTARIO

CANADIAN FORESTRY SERVICE

GOVERNMENT OF CANADA

1988

INFORMATION REPORT O-X-392

©Minister of Supply and Services Canada 1988
Catalogue No. Fo 46-14/392E
ISBN: 0-662-16069-X
ISSN: 0832-7122

Copies of this publication are available at no charge from:

Communications Services
Great Lakes Forestry Centre
Canadian Forestry Service
Government of Canada
P.O. Box 490
Sault Ste. Marie, Ontario
P6A 5M7

Microfiches of this publication may be purchased from:

Micromedia Inc.
Place du Portage
165, Hotel-de-Ville
Hull, Quebec
J8X 3X2

Syme, P.D. and Nystrom, K.L. 1988. Insects and mites associated with Ontario forests: classification, common names, main hosts, and importance. Gov't of Can., Can. For. Ser., Sault Ste. Marie, Ontario. Inf. Rep. O-X-392. 131p.

ABSTRACT

This report was prepared to facilitate the use of scientific and common names of insects and mites dealt with by the forestry community of Ontario and includes most of the species recorded by the Forest Insect and Disease Survey over the past 35 years. Insects and mites are arranged alphabetically by genus and species. Information provided for each entry includes order, family name, common name, host plant or insect type and a rating of current importance.

RÉSUMÉ

Préparé en vue de faciliter l'emploi des noms scientifiques et vernaculaires des insectes et acariens auxquels les chercheurs forestiers de l'Ontario ont affaire, le présent rapport comporte la plupart des espèces enregistrées par le Relevé des insectes et des maladies des arbres forestiers au cours des 40 dernières années. La disposition adoptée est l'ordre alphabétique par genre et espèce. Pour chaque entrée l'information fournie comprend l'ordre, le nom de famille, le nom vernaculaire, la plante-hôte ou le type d'insecte et un paramètre d'importance courant.

ACKNOWLEDGMENTS

We wish to acknowledge the excellent technical contributions of Mrs. Lesley Cree and Miss Céline Handfield in the preparation of this report.

Frontispiece. *Nymphalis antiopa* L. (mourning cloak butterfly).

TABLE OF CONTENTS

Cover photo: Big poplar sphinx larva.

INTRODUCTION

This report, originally prepared by W.J. Miller and O.H. Lindquist in 1971, revised first in 1975 and again in 1981 by O.H. Lindquist and P.D. Syme, is an alphabetical listing by genus and species of most insects and mites received by the Forest Insect and Disease Survey in Ontario over the past 42 years. Also included are a few insects that are serious pests in other parts of Canada, but are not currently found in Ontario. The order and family name are given for each species. Only in one family, the Tortricidae (order Lepidoptera), have we attempted to separate subfamilies; we have used the term "Olethreutinae" where applicable. The scientific names are those in current use at the time of publication, and are taken from the most recent checklists, catalogues and other literature. Most of the names are those in current use at the Biosystematics Research Centre, Agriculture Canada, which is the custodian of the Canadian National Collection of Insects. Common names were drawn from the entomological literature and in some cases in which no common name existed, a descriptive name was devised by the authors. Generalized names were used for less common species. In large part, the common names used have been approved by the Entomological Society of Canada and the Entomological Society of America. Great care has been taken to standardize the way in which authority names have been presented. The main host plant(s), if known, are listed for each species of phytophagous forest insect. The designation "general feeder" pertains to a combination of coniferous and deciduous hosts. Other non-phytophagous or subterranean forest insects as well as agricultural and household pests are, for the most part, classified only by insect type, such as parasite or predator. Each entry includes a current importance rating. These ratings are defined as follows:

A of major importance, capable of killing or severely damaging trees or shrubs;

B of moderate importance, capable of sporadic or localized injury to trees or shrubs;

C of minor importance, not known to present a threat to living trees or shrubs;

D beneficial, killing other insect pests;

E of major importance in other parts of North America but not currently known to occur in Ontario;

F insects of forest products or insects associated with the forest environment but not attacking forest trees or shrubs;

G miscellaneous insects of no consequence in forestry.

This compilation should be useful to any individual who is periodically confronted with unfamiliar scientific names of forest insects and mites in Ontario. It should also serve as a general reference for stenographic and library staff, various other support groups of federal and provincial governments, and academic institutions in which forestry and related disciplines are taught. It is *not* intended as a nomenclatural authority for reporting of research.

ALPHABETICAL LISTING
BY GENUS AND SPECIES

ALPHABETICAL LISTING BY GENUS AND SPECIES

SCIENTIFIC NAME	ORDER	FAMILY	COMMON NAME	MAIN HOST PLANT(S) OR INSECT TYPE	IMPORTANCE RATING
Abagrotis					
alternata (Grt.)	Lepidoptera	Noctuidae	owlet moth	unknown	C
Abgrallaspis					
ithacae (Ferris)	Homoptera	Coccidae	hemlock scale	spruce, fir, hemlock	C
Acantholyda					
erythrocephala (L.)	Hymenoptera	Pamphiliidae	pine false webworm	pine	A
luteomaculata (Cress.)	"	"	webspinning sawfly	pine	C
maculiventris (Nort.)	"	"	" "	spruce, balsam fir	C
Aceria (= *Eriophyes* in part)					
caulis (Cook)	Acari	Eriophyidae	velvet gall mite	walnut	C
sp. nr. *dispar* (Nal.)	"	"	aspen leaf mite	aspen	B
parapopuli Keifer	"	"	poplar budgall mite	poplar	C
rudis complex	"	"	birch budgall mite	birch	C
ulmi (Gar.)	"	"	elm leafgall mite	elm	C
Acericecis (See also *Cecidomyia* and *Contarinia*)					
ocellaris (O.S.)	Diptera	Cecidomyiidae	ocellate gall midge	maple	C
Achatia (= *Morrisonia* in part)					
distincta Hbn.	Lepidoptera	Noctuidae	owlet moth	deciduous	C
Acholla					
multispinosa DeG.	Hemiptera	Reduviidae	assassin bug	predator	D
Acleris					
braunana (McD.)	Lepidoptera	Tortricidae	alder leafroller	alder, birch	C
caliginosana (Wlk.)	"	"	birch leafroller	birch, alder	C
celiana (Rob.)	"	"	leafroller	deciduous	C
chalybeana (Fern.)	"	"	lesser maple leafroller	maple	C
cornana (McD.)	"	"	dogwood leafroller	dogwood, alder	C

SCIENTIFIC NAME	ORDER	FAMILY	COMMON NAME	MAIN HOST PLANT(S) OR INSECT TYPE	IMPORTANCE RATING
Acleris					
emargana (F.)	Lepidoptera	Tortricidae	leafroller	willow, poplar	C
fuscana (B. & Bsk.)	"	"	small aspen leaftier	deciduous	C
implexana (Wlk.)	"	"	leafroller	willow	C
hudsoniana (Wlk.)	"	"	"	general feeder	C
kearfottana (McD.)	"	"	"	ground plants	F
logiana placidana (Rob.)	"	"	blackheaded birch leaffolder	birch	C
maccana (Treit.)	"	"	leafroller	deciduous	C
minuta (Rob.)	"	"	yellowheaded fireworm	leatherleaf	F
nigrolinea (Rob.)	"	"	leafroller	deciduous	C
nivisellana (Wlsm.)	"	"	"	mountain ash	C
oxycoccana (Pack.)	"	"	"	blueberry	F
semiannula (Rob.)	"	"	solitary birch leafroller	birch	C
subnivana (Wlk.)	"	"	leafroller	oak	C
variana (Fern.)	"	"	eastern blackheaded budworm	spruce, balsam fir, hemlock	B
Acmaeops					
pratensis (Laich.)	Coleoptera	Cerambycidae	longhorned beetle	spruce	C
proteus (Kby.)	"	"	" "	coniferous	C
Acordulecera					
dorsalis Say	Hymenoptera	Tenthredinidae	sawfly	oak, nut trees	C
Acraspis					
erinacei (Beut.)	Hymenoptera	Cynipidae	gall wasp	oak	C
Acrobasis					
angusella Grt.	Lepidoptera	Pyralidae	leafstem borer	hickory, walnut	C
betulella Hlst.	"	"	birch tubemaker	white birch	C
caryae Grt.	"	"	hickory shoot borer	hickory	C
caryivorella Rag.	"	"	shoot borer-and-tier	hickory, walnut	C
comptoniella Hlst.	"	"	sweetfern casebearer	sweetfern	F

SCIENTIFIC NAME	ORDER	FAMILY	COMMON NAME	MAIN HOST PLANT(S) OR INSECT TYPE	IMPORTANCE RATING
Acrobasis					
demotella Grt.	Lepidoptera	Pyralidae	walnut shoot moth	hickory, walnut, butternut	A
juglandis (LeB.)	"	"	pecan leaf casebearer	walnut, hickory	C
kearfottella Dyar	"	"	tubemaker	hickory, butternut	C
rubrifasciella Pack.	"	"	alder tubemaker	alder	C
stigmella Dyar	"	"	hickory bud-and-shoot borer	hickory	C
sylviella Ely	"	"	ironwood tubemaker	ironwood	C
tricolorella Grt.	"	"	tubemaker	deciduous	C
Acrocercops					
albinatella Cham.	Lepidoptera	Gracillariidae	leafminer moth	red oak	C
Acronicta					
afflicta Grt.	Lepidoptera	Noctuidae	owlet moth	oak	C
americana (Harr.)	"	"	American daggermoth	deciduous	C
clarescens Gn.	"	"	owlet moth	"	C
dactylina Grt.	"	"	alder daggermoth	"	C
fragilis (Gn.)	"	"	fragile daggermoth	"	C
funeralis G. & R.	"	"	paddle caterpillar	"	C
furcifera Gn.	"	"	forked daggermoth	cherry	C
grisea Wlk.	"	"	gray daggermoth	"	C
haesitata (Grt.)	"	"	owlet moth	oak	C
hasta Gn.	"	"	cherry daggermoth	cherry	C
impleta Wlk.	"	"	owlet moth	deciduous	C
impressa Wlk.	"	"	willow daggermoth	"	C
innotata Gn.	"	"	birch daggermoth	"	C
interrupta Gn.	"	"	owlet moth	deciduous	C
lanceolaria (Grt.)	"	"	" "	general feeder	C
leporina (L.)	"	"	poplar daggermoth	deciduous	C
lepusculina Gn.	"	"	cottonwood daggermoth	"	C
lithospila Grt.	"	"	owlet moth	oak	C
morula G. & R.	"	"	ochre daggermoth	deciduous	C
oblinita (J.E. Smith)	"	"	smeared daggermoth	general feeder	C
ovata Grt.	"	"	oak daggermoth	oak	C
quadrata Grt.	"	"	plum daggermoth	cherry, plum	C
radcliffei (Harv.)	"	"	owlet moth	deciduous	C

SCIENTIFIC NAME	ORDER	FAMILY	COMMON NAME	MAIN HOST PLANT(S) OR INSECT TYPE	IMPORTANCE RATING
Acronicta					
retardata (Wlk.)	Lepidoptera	Noctuidae	maple daggermoth	maple	C
sperata Grt.	"	"	owlet moth	deciduous	C
superans Gn.	"	"	"	"	C
tristis Sm.	"	"	sad daggermoth	beech, maple	C
vinnula (Grt.)	"	"	elm daggermoth	white elm	C
Actebia					
fennica (Tausch.)	Lepidoptera	Noctuidae	black army cutworm	general feeder	A
Actias					
luna (L.)	Lepidoptera	Saturniidae	luna moth	deciduous	C
Adalia					
bipunctata (L.)	Coleoptera	Coccinellidae	twospotted lady beetle	predator	D
frigida (Schn.)	"	"	lady beetle	"	D
Adelges					
abietis (L.)	Homoptera	Phylloxeridae (= Adelgidae)	eastern spruce gall adelgid	spruce	B
cooleyi (Gill.)	"	"	Cooley spruce gall adelgid	spruce, Douglas-fir	C
lariciatus (Patch)	"	"	spruce gall adelgid	spruce, larch	B
piceae (Ratz.)	"	"	balsam woolly adelgid	balsam fir	E
strobilobius (Kltb.)	"	"	pale spruce gall adelgid	black spruce, larch	C
Adoxophyes					
negundana (McD.)	Lepidoptera	Tortricidae	leafroller moth	Manitoba maple	C
Adoxus					
obscurus L.	Coleoptera	Chrysomelidae	leaf beetle	deciduous	C
Aeschna					
spp.	Odonata	Aeschnidae	dragon fly	predator	D
Aethalura					
intertexta (Wlk.)	Lepidoptera	Geometridae	looper	deciduous	C

SCIENTIFIC NAME	ORDER	FAMILY	COMMON NAME	MAIN HOST PLANT(S) OR INSECT TYPE	IMPORTANCE RATING
Aethes					
rutilana (Hbn.)	Lepidoptera	Cochylidae	Pale juniper webworm	juniper	C
Agathis					
pumila (Ratz.)	Hymenoptera	Braconidae	parasite	larch casebearer	C
Aglais (see also *Nymphalis*)					
milberti Godt.	Lepidoptera	Nymphalidae	Milbert's tortoiseshell	nettles	F
Agonopterix					
argillacea (Wlsm.)	Lepidoptera	Oecophoridae	micro moth	deciduous	C
nigrinotella (Bsk.)	"	"	"	hop-tree	C
robiniella (Pack.)	"	"	"	locust	C
Agonum					
sinuatum Dej.	Coleoptera	Carabidae	ground beetle	predator	D
Agrilus					
anxius Gory	Coleoptera	Buprestidae	bronze birch borer	birch	B
billineatus (Web.)	"	"	twolined chestnut borer	oak, chestnut	C
egenus Gory	"	"	flatheaded wood borer	locust, hickory	B
liragus B. & B.	"	"	bronze poplar borer	poplar	B
politus (Say)	"	"	willow gall limb borer	willow	C
ruficollis (F.)	"	"	rednecked cane borer	blackberry	C
Agriotes					
collaris LeC.	Coleoptera	Elateridae	click beetle	soil insect	F
fucosis LeC.	"	"	"	"	F
limosus (LeC.)	"	"	little brown click beetle	"	F
mancus (Say)	"	"	wheat wireworm	agricultural pest	F
stabilis LeC.	"	"	"	soil insect	F
Agriphila (= *Crambus* in part)					
ruricolella (Zell.)	Lepidoptera	Pyralidae	webworm	grasses	F
vulgivagella (Clem.)	"	"	vagabond crambus	"	F

SCIENTIFIC NAME	ORDER	FAMILY	COMMON NAME	MAIN HOST PLANT(S) OR INSECT TYPE	IMPORTANCE RATING
Agromyza					
aristata Mall. (= *ulmi* Frost)	Diptera	Agromyzidae	elm agromyzid leafminer	elm	C
melampyga Loew	"	"	mock orange leafminer	mock orange	C
Agroperina					
dubitans cogitata (Sm.)	Lepidoptera	Noctuidae	cutworm	grass	F
d. dubitans (Wlk.)	"	"	"	"	F
Agrotis					
mollis Wlk.	Lepidoptera	Noctuidae	cutworm	unknown	C
ipsilon (Hufn.)	"	"	black cutworm	general feeder	C
Alabama					
argillacea (Hbn.)	Lepidoptera	Noctuidae	cotton leafworm	unknown here	F
Alaus					
oculatus (L.)	Coleoptera	Elateridae	large-eyed click beetle	predator	D
Allantus					
basalis (Klug)	Hymenoptera	Tenthredinidae	rose sawfly	birch, rose	C
Alobates					
pennsylvanica DeG.	Coleoptera	Tenebrionidae	beetle	household pest	G
Alsophila					
pometaria (Harr.)	Lepidoptera	Geometridae	fall cankerworm	deciduous	A
Altica (See also *Macrohaltica*)					
carinata Germ.	Coleoptera	Chrysomelidae	elm flea beetle	elm	B
chalybea (Ill.)	"	"	grape flea beetle	grape	F
corni Woods	"	"	dogwood flea beetle	dogwood	C
rosae Woods	"	"	rose flea beetle	rose	C
tombacina shoemakeri Schaeff.	"	"	flea beetle	ground plants	F

SCIENTIFIC NAME	ORDER	FAMILY	COMMON NAME	MAIN HOST PLANT(S) OR INSECT TYPE	IMPORTANCE RATING
Alypia					
langtoni Couper	Lepidoptera	Agaristidae	fireweed caterpillar	fireweed	F
octomaculata (F.)	"	"	eightspotted forester	grapevine, virginia creeper	C
Amara					
interstitialis (Dej.)	Coleoptera	Carabidae	ground beetle	predator	D
Amathes (See *Xestia*)					
Amauronematus					
fallax (Lep.)	Hymenoptera	Tenthredinidae	sawfly	white birch	C
gracilis Marl.	"	"	"	willow	C
histrio (Lep.)	"	"	"	"	C
neglectus (Kby.)	"	"	"	"	C
Amblyptilia (= *Platyptilia* in part)					
pica (Wlsm.)	Lepidoptera	Pterophoridae	plume moth	unknown	C
(= *punctidactyla* Haw.)					
Ametastegia					
recens (Say)	Hymenoptera	Tenthredinidae	willow sawfly	deciduous	C
Ammophila					
arvensis (Lep.)	Hymenoptera	Sphecidae	wasp	predator	D
Ampedus					
apicatus Say	Coleoptera	Elateridae	click beetle	soil insect	F
luctuosus (LeC.)	"	"	"	"	F
melanotoides Brown	"	"	"	"	F
melsheimeri Leng	"	"	"	"	F
mixtus Hbst.	"	"	"	"	F
pullus Germ.	"	"	"	"	F
semicinctus Rand.	"	"	"	"	F
Amphibolips					
confluenta (Harr.)	Hymenoptera	Cynipidae	spongy oak apple gall	red oak	C
quercusinanis (O.S.)	"	"	large oak apple gall	" "	C

SCIENTIFIC NAME	ORDER	FAMILY	COMMON NAME	MAIN HOST PLANT(S) OR INSECT TYPE	IMPORTANCE RATING
Amphipyra pyramidoides Gn.	Lepidoptera	Noctuidae	rearhumped caterpillar	deciduous	C
Anacampsis (= Compsolechia) innocuella (Zell.)	Lepidoptera	Gelechiidae	darkheaded aspen leafroller	poplar	C
niveopulvella (Chamb.)	"	"	paleheaded aspen leafroller	"	C
Anacamptodes ephyraria (Wlk.) *(larvaria* Gn. see *Iridopsis) vellivolata* (Hlst.)	Lepidoptera	Geometridae	looper	deciduous	C
	"	"	"	coniferous	C
Anagasta kuehniella (Zell.)	Lepidoptera	Pyralidae	Mediterranean flour moth	household pest	G
Anagoga occiduaria (Wlk.)	Lepidoptera	Geometridae	looper	deciduous	C
Anagrapha falcifera (Kby.)	Lepidoptera	Noctuidae	celery looper	agricultural pest	G
Anaplectoides pressus (Grt.)	Lepidoptera	Noctuidae	dagger moth	unknown	C
Anathix puta (G. & R.)	Lepidoptera	Noctuidae	poplar catkin moth	poplar	C
Anatis labiculata (Say)	Coleoptera	Coccinellidae	fifteenspotted lady beetle	predator	D
mali (Say)	"	"	eyespotted lady beetle	"	D
Anavitrinella pampinaria (Gn.)	Lepidoptera	Geometridae	cranberry spanworm	general feeder	C

SCIENTIFIC NAME	ORDER	FAMILY	COMMON NAME	MAIN HOST PLANT(S) OR INSECT TYPE	IMPORTANCE RATING
Ancylis					
burgessiana (Zell.)	Lepidoptera	Olethreutinae	oak leaffolder	red oak	C
discigerana (Wlk.)	"	"	yellow birch leaffolder	birch	C
fuscociliana (Clem.)	"	"	elm leaffolder	elm, oak	C
mediofasciana (Clem.)	"	"	serviceberry leaffolder	serviceberry, cherry	C
mira Heinr.	"	"	alder leaffolder	alder	C
nubeculana (Clem.)	"	"	cherry leaffolder	deciduous	C
spiraeifoliana (Clem.)	"	"	ninebark leaffolder	ninebark	C
subaequana (Zell.)	"	"	willow leaffolder	willow	C
Andricus					
quercusflocci (Walsh)	Hymenoptera	Cynipidae	gall wasp	white oak	C
Androchirus					
erythropus Kby.	Coleoptera	Alleculidae	combclawed beetle	unknown	F
Anisocalvia					
duodecimmaculata Gebl.	Coleoptera	Coccinellidae	twelvespotted lady beetle	predator	D
quatuordecimguttata L.	"	"	fourteenspotted lady beetle	"	D
Anisota (see also *Dryocampa*)					
finlaysoni Riotte	Lepidoptera	Citheroniidae	shorthorned oakworm	oak	A
senatoria (J.E. Smith)	"	"	orangestriped oakworm	oak	A
stigma (F.)	"	"	spiny oakworm	"	C
virginiensis (Drury)	"	"	pinkstriped oakworm	"	B
Anobium					
punctatum (DeG.)	Coleoptera	Anobiidae	furniture beetle	dry wood	F
Anomoea					
laticlavia (Forst.)	Coleoptera	Chrysomelidae	claycolored leaf beetle	deciduous	C
Anomogyna					
elimata (Gn.)	Lepidoptera	Noctuidae	chameleon caterpillar	coniferous	C
perquiritata (Morr.)	"	"	gray spruce cutworm	"	C

SCIENTIFIC NAME	ORDER	FAMILY	COMMON NAME	MAIN HOST PLANT(S) OR INSECT TYPE	IMPORTANCE RATING
Anopheles					
quadrimaculatus Say	Diptera	Culicidae	common malaria mosquito	biting flies	F
Anoplodera					
biforis (Newm.)	Coleoptera	Cerambycidae	longhorn beetle	general feeder	C
chrysocoma (Oliv.)	"	"	"	unknown	C
nigrella (Say)	"	"	"	"	C
pubera (Say)	"	"	"	"	C
sanguinea LeC.	"	"	"	"	C
sexmaculata (L.)	"	"	"	"	C
vittata (Swed.)	"	"	"	general feeder	C
Anoplonyx					
canadensis Hgtn.	Hymenoptera	Tenthredinidae	onelined larch sawfly	larch	C
luteipes (Cress.)	"	"	threelined larch sawfly	"	C
Antaeotricha					
leucillana (Zell.)	Lepidoptera	Oecophoridae	micro moth	deciduous	C
(= *algidella* Wlk.)					
schlaegeri (Zell.)	"	"	"	birch	C
Anthaxia					
aeneogaster Cast.	Coleoptera	Buprestidae	flatheaded wood borer	unknown	C
viridifrons Gory	"	"	hickory twig borer	elm, hickory	C
Antheraea					
polyphemus (Cram.)	Lepidoptera	Saturniidae	polyphemus moth	deciduous	C
Anthophila (See *Choreutis*)					
Anthophilax					
attenuatus (Hald.)	Coleoptera	Cerambycidae	mottled longhorned beetle	decaying hardwoods	C
malachiticus (Hald.)	"	"	green longhorned beetle	"	C
Antispila					
cornifoliella Clem.	Lepidoptera	Heliozelidae	dogwood leafminer	dogwood	C
nysaefoliella Clem.	"	"	tupelo leafminer	blackgum	C

SCIENTIFIC NAME	ORDER	FAMILY	COMMON NAME	MAIN HOST PLANT(S) OR INSECT TYPE	IMPORTANCE RATING
Apamea *amputatrix* (Fitch)	Lepidoptera	Noctuidae	yellowheaded cutworm	not known	F
Apantesis *parthenice* (Kby.)	Lepidoptera	Arctiidae	tiger moth	general feeder	C
Apateticus *bracteatus* (Fitch)	Hemiptera	Pentatomidae	stink bug	predator	D
cynicus (Say)	"	"	"	"	D
Aphania (See *Apotomis*)					
Aphelia (See also *Xenotemna*) *alleniana* (Fern.)	Lepidoptera	Tortricidae	pine-and-clover tier	pine, clover	C
Aphis *maculatae* (Oestl.)	Homoptera	Aphididae	spotted poplar aphid	poplar	C
pomi (DeG.)	"	"	apple aphid	apple	F
Aphodius *erraticus* L.	Coleoptera	Scarabaeidae	scarab beetle	unknown	C
fimetarius (L.)	"	"	"	"	C
fossor L.	"	"	"	"	C
Aphrophora *cribrata* (Wlk.)	Homoptera	Cercopidae	pine spittlebug	nymphs and adults on conifers	B
parallela (Say)	"	"	spruce spittlebug	adults on conifers	C
saratogensis (Fitch)	"	"	Saratoga spittlebug	adults on pine	B
Apion *longirostre* Oliv.	Coleoptera	Curculionidae	hollyhock weevil	hollyhock	F
nigrum Hbst.	"	"	black locust seed weevil	black locust	C
simile Kby.	"	"	birch catkin weevil	birch	C

SCIENTIFIC NAME	ORDER	FAMILY	COMMON NAME	MAIN HOST PLANT(S) OR INSECT TYPE	IMPORTANCE RATING
Apoda (= *Limacodes*)					
y-inversum (Pack.)	Lepidoptera	Limacodidae	slug caterpillar	beech	C
Apotomis (= *Aphania* in part)					
albeolana (Zell.)	Lepidoptera	Olethreutinae	leafroller	birch	C
capreana (Hbn.)	"	"	"	deciduous	C
deceptana (Kft.)	"	"	"	aspen	C
dextrana (McD.)	"	"	green aspen leafroller	"	C
funerea (Meyr.)	"	"	leafroller	deciduous	C
tertiana (McD.)	"	"	"	"	C
Archiearis (= *Brephos*)					
infans (Mösch.)	Lepidoptera	Geometridae	looper	deciduous	C
Archips					
alberta (McD.)	Lepidoptera	Tortricidae	spruce cone moth	spruce	C
argyrospila (Wlk.)	"	"	fruittree leafroller	deciduous	C
cerasivorana (Fitch)	"	"	uglynest caterpillar	cherry	B
dissitana (Grt.)	"	"	spruce needle moth	coniferous	C
fervidana (Clem.)	"	"	oak webworm	oak	C
infumatana (Zell.)	"	"	hickory webworm	walnut, hickory	C
mortuana Kft.	"	"	duskyback leafroller	deciduous	C
myricana (McD.)	"	"	leafroller	"	C
negundana (Dyar)	"	"	larger boxelder leaf-roller	Manitoba maple	B
packardiana (Fern.)	"	"	spring spruce needle moth	spruce, fir	C
purpurana Clem.	"	"	omnivorous leafroller	deciduous	C
rosana (L.)	"	"	European leafroller	"	C
semiferana Wlk.	"	"	oak leafroller	oak	C
striana (Fern.)	"	"	lined spruce needleworm	spruce, fir	C
Arctia					
caja (L.)	Lepidoptera	Arctiidae	garden tiger moth	spruce, fir	C

SCIENTIFIC NAME	ORDER	FAMILY	COMMON NAME	MAIN HOST PLANT(S) OR INSECT TYPE	IMPORTANCE RATING
Arge					
clavicornis (F.)	Hymenoptera	Argidae	willow argid	deciduous	C
pectoralis (Leach)	"	"	birch sawfly	birch, alder, hazelnut, hawthorn	B
scapularis (Klug.)	"	"	oak sawfly	oak, elm, birch, alder	B
Argyresthia					
abies Free.	Lepidoptera	Yponomeutidae	balsam fir tipminer	balsam fir	C
affinis Braun	"	"	juniper leafminer	red juniper	C
aureoargentella Brower	"	"	cedar leafminer	cedar	B
canadensis Free.	"	"	" "	"	B
freyella Wlsm.	"	"	red juniper leafminer	red juniper	B
goedartella (L.)	"	"	birch ermine moth	birch	C
laricella Kft.	"	"	larch shoot moth	larch	B
mariana Free.	"	"	black spruce tipminer	black spruce	C
oreasella Clem.	"	"	cherry shoot borer	cherry	C
picea Free.	"	"	white spruce tipminer	white spruce	C
pygmaeella (Hbn.)	"	"	willow leaftier	willow	C
thuiella (Pack.)	"	"	arborvitae leafminer	cedar	A
Argyrotaenia					
juglandana (Fern.)	Lepidoptera	Tortricidae	hickory leafroller	hickory	C
mariana (Fern.)	"	"	graybanded leafroller	deciduous	C
occultana Free.	"	"	fall spruce needle moth	coniferous	C
pinatubana (Kft.)	"	"	pine tube moth	white pine	C
quadrifasciana (Fern.)	"	"	fourlined leafroller	cherry, serviceberry	C
quercifoliana Fitch	"	"	tortricid oakworm	oak	C
tabulana Free.	"	"	jack pine tube moth	jack pine	C
velutinana (Wlk.)	"	"	redbanded leafroller	general feeder	C
Arhopalus					
foveicollis (Harr.)	Coleoptera	Cerambycidae	pitted longhorned beetle	unknown	C
Aristotelia					
fungivorella (Clem.)	Lepidoptera	Gelechiidae	micro moth	willow	C

SCIENTIFIC NAME	ORDER	FAMILY	COMMON NAME	MAIN HOST PLANT(S) OR INSECT TYPE	IMPORTANCE RATING
Arthromacra aenea Say	Coleoptera	Lagriidae	metallic beetle	scavenger	F
Artogeia (= Pieris) rapae (L.)	Lepidoptera	Pieridae	imported cabbageworm	cabbage	G
Asemum striatum (L.)	Coleoptera	Cerambycidae	opaque sawyer	pine	C
Asiphum rosettei Max.	Homoptera	Aphididae	aspen aphid	poplar	C
Asterocampa celtis (Bdv. & LeC.)	Lepidoptera	Nymphalidae	hackberry butterfly	hackberry	C
Asterolecanium variolosum (Ratz.)	Homoptera	Asterolecaniidae	golden oak scale	oak, chestnut	C
Atomacera debilis Say	Hymenoptera	Argidae	trefoil sawfly	trefoil	F
Atrusca quercuscentricola (O.S.) (= Cynips centricola (O.S.)	Hymenoptera	Cynipidae	spotted oak apple	oak	C
Attelabus bipustulatis F.	Coleoptera	Curculionidae	leafrolling weevil	deciduous	C
Atteva punctella (Cramer)	Lepidoptera	Yponomeutidae	ailanthus webworm	tree of heaven	C
Autographa ampla (Wlk.) mappa (G. & R.)	Lepidoptera "	Noctuidae "	dagger moth "	deciduous shrubs, plants	C C
Automeris io (F.)	Lepidoptera	Saturniidae	io moth	deciduous	C

SCIENTIFIC NAME	ORDER	FAMILY	COMMON NAME	MAIN HOST PLANT(S) OR INSECT TYPE	IMPORTANCE RATING
Baileya					
dormitans (Gn.)	Lepidoptera	Nycteolidae	macro moth	deciduous	C
doubledayi (Gn.)	"	"	"	alder	C
ophthalmica (Gn.)	"	"	"	deciduous	C
Baliosus					
nervosus Panz.	Coleoptera	Chrysomelidae	basswood leafminer	basswood	B
Balsa					
malana (Fitch)	Lepidoptera	Noctuidae	owlet moth	apple	C
Banasa					
dimidiata Say	Hemiptera	Pentatomidae	banasa stink bug	predator	D
Barbara					
mappana Free.	Lepidoptera	Olethreutinae	cone moth	balsam fir, white spruce	C
Basilarchia (= *Limenitis*)					
archippus (Cram.)	Lepidoptera	Nymphalidae	viceroy	deciduous	C
a. arthemis (Drury)	"	"	white admiral	"	C
arthemis astyanax (F.)	"	"	redspotted purple	"	C
Bassareus					
sellatus Suffr.	Coleoptera	Chrysomelidae	leaf beetle	deciduous	C
Batrachedra					
praeangusta (Haw.)	Lepidoptera	Cosmopterygidae	poplar shoot moth	poplar	C
Battaristis					
vittella (Bsk.)	Lepidoptera	Gelechiidae	micro moth	pine	C
Battus					
philenor (L.)	Lepidoptera	Papilionidae	pipevine swallowtail	pipevine	C
Besma					
endropiaria (G. & R.)	Lepidoptera	Geometridae	looper	deciduous	C
quercivoraria (Gn.)	"	"	"	"	C

SCIENTIFIC NAME	ORDER	FAMILY	COMMON NAME	MAIN HOST PLANT(S) OR INSECT TYPE	IMPORTANCE RATING
Bessa					
harveyi (Towns.)	Diptera	Tachinidae	parasitic fly	parasite	D
Bibarrambla					
allenella (Wlsm.)	Lepidoptera	Oecophoridae	birch-and-alder leaftier	birch, alder	C
Bibio					
xanthopus Wied.	Diptera	Bibionidae	March fly	vegetable matter	F
Biston					
betularia cognataria (Gn.)	Lepidoptera	Geometridae	pepper-and-salt moth	deciduous	C
Blattella					
germanica (L.)	Orthoptera	Blattidae	German cockroach	household pest	G
Blepharida					
rhois Forst.	Coleoptera	Chrysomelidae	sumac leaf beetle	sumac	C
Bomolocha					
abalienalis (Wlk.)	Lepidoptera	Noctuidae	owlet moth	deciduous	C
baltimoralis (Gn.)	"	"	"	maple	C
bijugalis (Wlk.)	"	"	"	dogwood	C
deceptalis (Wlk.)	"	"	basswood owlet moth	basswood	C
palparia (Wlk.)	"	"	owlet moth	deciduous	C
Bondia					
comonana (Kft.)	Lepidoptera	Carposinidae	micro moth	cherry	C
Brachyacantha					
felina (F.)	Coleoptera	Coccinellidae	lady beetle	predator	D
ursina (F.)	"	"	"	"	D
(*Brachyrhinus*) see *Otiorhynchus*					
Brachys					
aerosus Melsh.	Coleoptera	Buprestidae	leafmining beetle	oak, aspen	C
rufescens N. & W.	"	"	"	unknown	C
ovatus (Weber)	"	"	"	oak, aspen	C

SCIENTIFIC NAME	ORDER	FAMILY	COMMON NAME	MAIN HOST PLANT(S) OR INSECT TYPE	IMPORTANCE RATING
(Brephos) see Archiearis					
Brochymena quadripustulata F.	Hemiptera	Pentatonidae	fourhumped stink bug	predator	D
Bucculatrix ainsliella Murt.	Lepidoptera	Lyonetiidae	oak skeletonizer	oak	C
canadensisella Cham.	"	"	birch skeletonizer	birch	A
Buprestis fasciata F.	Coleoptera	Buprestidae	flatheaded wood borer	general	C
maculativentris Say	"	"	ventrally spotted buprestid	balsam fir, spruce	C
nuttali Kby.	"	"	flatheaded wood borer	coniferous	C
striata F.	"	"	"	"	C
Cabera erythemaria Gn.	Lepidoptera	Geometridae	looper	willow	C
variolaria Gn.	"	"	"	deciduous	C
Caenurgina crassiuscula (Haw.)	Lepidoptera	Noctuidae	clover looper	clover	F
Caliroa cerasi (L.)	Hymenoptera	Tenthredinidae	pearslug sawfly	mountain ash, fruit trees	C
fasciata (Nort.)	"	"	oakslug sawfly	oak	C
obsoleta (Nort.)	"	"	"	"	C
Callidium frigidam Casey	Coleoptera	Cerambycidae	longhorned beetle	dead cedar and juniper	C
violaceum (L.)	"	"	"	dead pine	C

SCIENTIFIC NAME	ORDER	FAMILY	COMMON NAME	MAIN HOST PLANT(S) OR INSECT TYPE	IMPORTANCE RATING
Calligrapha					
alni Schaeff.	Coleoptera	Chrysomelidae	russet alder leaf beetle	alder	C
amator Brown	"	"	basswood leaf beetle	basswood	C
apicalis Notm.	"	"	alder leaf beetle	alder	C
confluens Schaeff.	"	"	alder leaf beetle	"	C
ignota Brown	"	"	birch leaf beetle	birch	C
multipunctata bigsbyana (Kby.)	"	"	willow leaf beetle	willow, poplar	C
philadelphica (L.)	"	"	dogwood leaf beetle	deciduous	C
rhoda Knab	"	"	hazel leaf beetle	hazel	C
scalaris (LeC.)	"	"	elm calligrapha	elm	C
tiliae Brown	"	"	basswood leaf beetle	basswood	C
Callirhytis					
cornigera (O. S.)	Hymenoptera	Cynipidae	horned oak gall wasp	oak	C
quercusfutilis (O. S.)	"	"	oak gall wasp	"	C
quercusgemmaria (Ashm.)	"	"	ribbed budgall wasp	"	C
quercusmodesta (O. S.)	"	"	oak gall wasp	"	C
quercusoperator (O. S.)	"	"	woolly blossomgall wasp	"	C
quercuspunctata (Bass.)	"	"	gouty oak gall wasp	"	C
seminator (Harr.)	"	"	wool sower wasp	"	C
tumifica (O. S.)	"	"	oak leafgall wasp	"	C
(Callophrys) see *Incisalia*					
Callopistria					
cordata (Ljungh)	Lepidoptera	Noctuidae	owlet moth	fern	F
Callosamia					
promethea (Drury)	Lepidoptera	Saturniidae	promethea moth	deciduous	C
Calopteryx					
maculata (Beauv.)	Odonata	Coenagrionidae	brown damselfly	predator	D

SCIENTIFIC NAME	ORDER	FAMILY	COMMON NAME	MAIN HOST PLANT(S) OR INSECT TYPE	IMPORTANCE RATING
Caloptilia (= *Gracillaria*)					
alnivorella (Cham.)	Lepidoptera	Gracillariidae	alder leafminer	alder	C
betulivora McD.	"	"	birch leafroller	birch	C
burgessiella (Zell.)	"	"	dogwood leafroller	dogwood	C
coroniella (Clem.)	"	"	birch leafroller	birch	C
fraxinella (Ely)	"	"	privet leafminer	ash	C
invariabilis (Braun)	"	"	cherry leafcone caterpillar	cherry	C
negundella (Cham.)	"	"	boxelder leafroller	Manitoba maple	C
rhoifoliella (Cham.)	"	"	sumac leafroller	sumac	C
sassafrasella (Cham.)	"	"	sassafras leafroller	sassafras	C
stigmatella (F.)	"	"	maple leafroller	maple	C
strictella (Wlk.)	"	"	birch leafroller	birch	C
syringella (F.)	"	"	lilac leafminer	lilac	B
Calosoma					
calidum (F.)	Coleoptera	Carabidae	fiery hunter	predator	D
frigidum Kby.	"	"	ground beetle	"	D
scrutator F.	"	"	"	"	D
Cameraria (= *Lithocolletis*)					
aceriella (Clem.)	Lepidoptera	Gracillariidae	maple leafblotch miner	maple	C
betulivora (Wlsm.)	"	"	birch leafblotch miner	birch	C
caryaefoliella (Clem.)	"	"	hickory leafblotch miner	hickory	C
cincinnatiella (Cham.)	"	"	gregarious oak leafminer	oak	C
fletcherella (Braun)	"	"	oak leafblotch miner	"	C
hamadryadella (Clem.)	"	"	solitary oak leafminer	"	B
hamameliella (Bsk.)	"	"	witch hazel leafblotch miner	witch hazel	C
macrocarpella (F. & B.)	"	"	oak leafblotch miner	oak	C
ostryarella (Cham.)	"	"	ironwood leafblotch miner	ironwood	C
quercivorella (Cham.)	"	"	oak leafblotch miner	oak	C
ulmella (Cham.)	"	"	elm leafblotch miner	elm	C

SCIENTIFIC NAME	ORDER	FAMILY	COMMON NAME	MAIN HOST PLANT(S) OR INSECT TYPE	IMPORTANCE RATING
Camnula					
pellucida (Scudd.)	Orthoptera	Acrididae	clearwinged grasshopper	ground plants	F
Campaea					
perlata (Gn.)	Lepidoptera	Geometridae	fringed looper	general feeder	C
Camponotus					
herculeanus (L.)	Hymenoptera	Formicidae	boreal carpenter ant	dry wood	C
noveaboracensis (Fitch)	"	"	red and black carpenter ant	"	C
pennsylvanicus (DeG.)	"	"	black carpenter ant	"	C
Canarsia					
ulmiarrosorella (Clem.)	Lepidoptera	Pyralidae	elm leaftier	elm	C
Cantharis					
bilineatus Say	Coleoptera	Cantharidae	twolined cantharid	predator	D
carolinus F.	"	"	Carolina cantharid	"	D
Caripeta					
angustiorata Wlk.	Lepidoptera	Geometridae	brown pine looper	coniferous	C
divisata Wlk.	"	"	gray spruce looper	"	C
piniata (Pack.)	"	"	pine looper	pine, spruce	C
Carposina					
fernaldana Bsk.	Lepidoptera	Carposinidae	micro moth	deciduous fruits	C
Carulaspis					
juniperi (Bouché)	Homoptera	Coccidae	juniper scale	juniper, cedar	C
Carynota					
stupida (Wlk.)	Homoptera	Membracidae	stupid treehopper	birch	C
Cassida					
rubiginosa Mull.	Coleoptera	Chrysomelidae	green tortoise beetle	thistles	F

SCIENTIFIC NAME	ORDER	FAMILY	COMMON NAME	MAIN HOST PLANT(S) OR INSECT TYPE	IMPORTANCE RATING
Catabena					
lineolata Wlk.	Lepidoptera	Noctuidae	owlet moth	ground plants	F
Catocala					
antinympha (Hbn.)	Lepidoptera	Noctuidae	sweetfern underwing	sweet fern	C
blandula Hlst.	"	"	grayblue underwing	hawthorne	C
briseis Edw.	"	"	Briseis underwing	poplar, willow	C
cara Gn.	"	"	darling underwing	willow	C
cerogama Gn.	"	"	yellowbanded under-wing	basswood, poplar	C
concumbens Wlk.	"	"	pink underwing	willow, trembling aspen	C
habilis Grt.	"	"	hickory underwing	butternut, ash	C
ilia (Cram.)	"	"	ilia underwing	red oak	C
piatrix Grt.	"	"	underwing moth	walnut, ash	C
relicta Wlk.	"	"	white underwing	poplar, willow	C
retecta Grt.	"	"	yellowgray underwing	hickory	C
sordida Grt.	"	"	blueberry underwing	blueberry	C
ultronia (Hbn.)	"	"	plum tree underwing	cherry, plum	C
unijuga Wlk.	"	"	oncemarried underwing	poplar, willow	C
Catoptria (= *Crambus* in part)					
latiradiella (Wlk.)	Lepidoptera	Pyralidae	webworm	grasses	F
Caulocampus					
acericaulis (MacG.)	Hymenoptera	Tenthredinidae	maple petiole borer	maple	C
Cecidomyia (See also *Acericecis* and *Contarinia*)					
pininopis O.S.	Diptera	Cecidomyiidae	jack pine midge	jack pine	C
(= *banksianae* Vock.)					
resinicola (O.S.)	"	"	jack pine resin midge	jack pine	C
(= *reeksi* Vock.)					
resinicoloides Wlms.	"	"	Monterey pine resin midge	jack pine	C
(= *accola* Vock.)					
verrucicola O. S.	"	"	linden wartgall midge	basswood	C
Celastrina					
ladon (Cram.)	Lepidoptera	Lycaenidae	spring azure	deciduous	C

SCIENTIFIC NAME	ORDER	FAMILY	COMMON NAME	MAIN HOST PLANT(S) OR INSECT TYPE	IMPORTANCE RATING
(Celerio) see Hyles					
(Cenopis) see Sparganothis					
Cepegillettea betulifoliae Granovsky	Homoptera	Aphididae	birch aphid	white birch	C
Cephalcia fascipennis (Cress.)	Hymenoptera	Pamphiliidae	spruce webspinning sawfly	spruce	C
frontalis (Westw.)	"	"	pine webspinning sawfly	red pine	C
fulviceps (Roh.)	"	"	pine webspinning sawfly	red and jack pine	C
marginata Midd.	"	"	red pine webspinning sawfly	red pine	C
Cephaloon lepturoides Newm.	Coleoptera	Cephaloidae	false leptura beetle	decayed coniferous wood	C
Ceratomia amyntor (Gey.)	Lepidoptera	Sphingidae	elm sphinx	deciduous	C
catalpae (Bdv.)	"	"	catalpa sphinx	catalpa	C
undulosa (Wlk.)	"	"	waved sphinx	ash	C
Cerura (See also *Furcula*) *scitiscripta canadensis* McD.	Lepidoptera	Notodontidae	forktailed caterpillar	poplar, willow	C
scitiscripta multiscripta Riley	"	"	"	"	C
Ceruraphis viburnicola (Gill.)	Homoptera	Aphididae	snowball aphid	viburnum	C
Chaitophorus populicola Thos.	Homoptera	Aphididae	smokeywinged poplar aphid	poplar	C
viminalis (Monell)	"	"	willow aphid	willow	C

SCIENTIFIC NAME	ORDER	FAMILY	COMMON NAME	MAIN HOST PLANT(S) OR INSECT TYPE	IMPORTANCE RATING
(*Chalcoides*) see *Crepidodera*					
Chalcophora					
fortis LeC.	Coleoptera	Buprestidae	flatheaded pine borer	dead pine	C
liberta Germ.	"	"	"	"	C
virginiensis (Drury)	"	"	Virginian buprestid	"	C
(*Chalepus*) see *Odontota*					
Charadra					
deridens (Gn.)	Lepidoptera	Noctuidae	masked hairy caterpillar	deciduous	C
Charadryas (= *Melitaea*)					
nycteis (Dbly.)	Lepidoptera	Nymphalidae	silvery checkerspot	poplar	C
Chelymorpha					
cassidea (F.)	Coleoptera	Chrysomelidae	argus tortoise beetle	milkweed, wild potato	F
Chilocorus					
stigma (Say)	Coleoptera	Coccinellidae	twicestabbed lady beetle	predator	D
Chionaspis					
americana Johns.	Homoptera	Diaspididae (Coccidae)	elm scurfy scale	elm	C
corni Cooley	"	"	dogwood scale	dogwood	C
furfura (Fitch)	"	"	scurfy scale	deciduous	C
lintneri Comst.	"	"	Lintner's scale	"	C
pinifoliae (Fitch)	"	"	pine needle scale	pine, spruce	C
Chionodes					
continuella Zell.	Lepidoptera	Gelechiidae	micro moth	white spruce	C
formosella (Murt.)	"	"	spring oak leafroller	oak	C
(= *vernella* Murt.)					
fuscomaculella Cham.	"	"	micro moth	oak	C
obscurusella Cham.	"	"	boxelder leafworm	maple, oak	C
terminimaculella Kft.	"	"	micro moth	poplar	C
thoraceochrella (Cham.)	"	"	"	oak	C

SCIENTIFIC NAME	ORDER	FAMILY	COMMON NAME	MAIN HOST PLANT(S) OR INSECT TYPE	IMPORTANCE RATING
Chlorochlamys chloroleucaria (Gn.)	Lepidoptera	Geometridae	blackberry looper	blackberry	C
Chlorochroa uhleri Say	Hemiptera	Pentatomidae	stink bug	unknown	C
Choreutis diana (Hbn.)	Lepidoptera	Choreutidae	micro moth	deciduous	C
pariana (Cl.)	"	"	apple-and-thorn skeletonizer	apple	C
Choristoneura conflictana (Wlk.)	Lepidoptera	Tortricidae	large aspen tortrix	poplar	B
fractivittana (Clem.)	"	"	brokenbanded leaf-roller	deciduous	C
fumiferana (Clem.)	"	"	eastern spruce budworm	balsam fir, spruce	A
obsoletana (Wlk.)	"	"	leafroller moth	white birch	C
pinus pinus Free.	"	"	jack pine budworm	jack pine	A
rosaceana (Harr.)	"	"	obliquebanded leaf-roller	deciduous	C
zapulata (Rob.)	"	"	leafroller moth	"	C
Chramesus hicoriae LeC.	Coleoptera	Scolytidae	hickory bark beetle	hickory	C
Chrysaster ostensackenella (Fitch)	Lepidoptera	Gracillariidae	ironwood leafblotch miner	ironwood	C
Chrysobothris dentipes (Germ.)	Coleoptera	Buprestidae	flatheaded wood borer	pine, larch	C
femorata (Oliv.)	"	"	flatheaded appletree borer	deciduous	C
floricola Gory	"	"	flatheaded wood borer	pine	C
harrisi Hentz	"	"	"	"	C
scabripennis Cast. & Gory	"	"	"	pine, hemlock	C
trinervia Kby.	"	"	"	pine	C

SCIENTIFIC NAME	ORDER	FAMILY	COMMON NAME	MAIN HOST PLANT(S) OR INSECT TYPE	IMPORTANCE RATING
Chrysochus auratus (F.)	Coleoptera	Chrysomelidae	dogbane beetle	dogbane	F
Chrysomela crotchi Brown	Coleoptera	Chrysomelidae	aspen leaf beetle	aspen	B
falsa Brown	"	"	willow-and-poplar leaf beetle	poplar, willow	C
k. knabi Brown	"	"	spotted willow leaf beetle	willow, poplar	C
laurentia Brown	"	"	willow-and-poplar leaf beetle	poplar, willow	C
lineatopunctata Forst.	"	"	willow-and-poplar leaf beetle	poplar	C
mainensis mainensis Bech.	"	"	alder leaf beetle	alder	C
scripta F.	"	"	cottonwood leaf beetle	poplar, willow	C
walshi Brown	"	"	balsam poplar leaf beetle	poplar	C
(Chrysopelia) see *Stilbosis*					
Chrysoperla (= Chrysopa) carnea (Steph.)	Neuroptera	Chrysopidae	common green lacewing	predator	D
Chrysops carbonarius Wlk.	Diptera	Tabanidae	deer fly	biting flies	F
Chrysoteuchia (= Crambus in part) *topiaria* (Zell.)	Lepidoptera	Pyralidae	webworm	grasses	F
Cicindela longilabris Say	Coleoptera	Cicindelidae	tiger beetle	predator	D
Cimberis elongatus (LeC.)	Coleoptera	Curculionidae	pine weevil	pine	C
Cimbex americana Leach	Hymenoptera	Cimbicidae	elm sawfly	deciduous	C

SCIENTIFIC NAME	ORDER	FAMILY	COMMON NAME	MAIN HOST PLANT(S) OR INSECT TYPE	IMPORTANCE RATING
Cinara					
abieticola (Cholodk.)	Homoptera	Aphididae	balsam fir aphid	balsam fir	C
banksiana P. & T.	"	"	jack pine aphid	jack pine	C
braggii (Gill.)	"	"	spruce aphid	spruce	C
coloradensis Gill.	"	"	"	white spruce	C
curvipes (Patch)	"	"	balsam fir aphid	balsam fir	C
fornacula Hottes	"	"	green spruce aphid	spruce	C
gracilis (Wils.) (= *canatra*)	"	"	jack pine aphid	jack pine	C
harmonia (Hottes)	"	"	red pine aphid	red pine	C
hottesi (G. & P.)	"	"	spruce aphid	spruce	C
laricifex (Fitch)	"	"	black larch aphid	larch	C
laricis (Htg.)	"	"	larch aphid	"	C
ontarioensis Brad.	"	"	jack pine needle aphid	jack pine	C
palmerae (Gill.)	"	"	spruce aphid	spruce	C
pinea (Mordvilko)	"	"	pine aphid	pine	C
pinivora Wils.	"	"	"	"	C
pergandei (Wils.)	"	"	jack pine aphid	jack pine	C
strobi (Fitch)	"	"	white pine aphid	white pine	C
Cincticornia					
pilulae (Beut.)	Diptera	Cecidomyiidae	oak pillgall midge	oak	C
Cingilia					
catenaria (Drury)	Lepidoptera	Geometridae	chainspotted geometer	coniferous, ground plants	C
Cisseps					
fulvicollis (Hbn.)	Lepidoptera	Amatidae	yellowcollared scapemoth	unknown	C
Cladara (= *Nyctobia*)					
atroliturata Wlk.	Lepidoptera	Geometridae	looper	deciduous	C
limitaria (Wlk.)	"	"	yellowlined conifer looper	coniferous	C
Clastoptera					
obtusa (Say)	Homoptera	Cercopidae	alder spittlebug	alder	C
proteus Fitch	"	"	dogwood spittlebug	dogwood	C

SCIENTIFIC NAME	ORDER	FAMILY	COMMON NAME	MAIN HOST PLANT(S) OR INSECT TYPE	IMPORTANCE RATING
Clemensia					
albata Pack.	Lepidoptera	Arctiidae	speckled gray footman	coniferous	C
Clepsis					
melaleucana (Wlk.)	Lepidoptera	Tortricidae	leafroller	coniferous	C
persicana (Fitch)	"	"	white triangle leafroller	"	C
Clostera (= Ichthyura)					
albosigma Fitch	Lepidoptera	Notodontidae	rustylined leaftier	poplar	C
apicalis (Wlk.)	"	"	redmarked tentmaker	"	C
inclusa (Hbn.)	"	"	poplar tentmaker	"	C
strigosa (Grt.)	"	"	poplar leaftier	"	C
Coccinella					
hieroglyphica kirbyi Crotch	Coleoptera	Coccinellidae	ladybeetle	predator	D
monticola Muls.	"	"	"	"	D
novemnotata Hbst.	"	"	ninespotted ladybeetle	"	D
transversoguttata richardsoni Brown	"	"	transverse ladybeetle	"	D
trifasciata perplexa Muls.	"	"	ladybeetle	"	D
trifasciata trifasciata L.	"	"	threebanded ladybeetle	"	D
unidecimpunctata L.	"	"	elevenspotted ladybeetle	"	D
Coccobaphes					
sanguinareus Uhl.	Hemiptera	Miridae	plant bug	unknown	C
Coleomegilla					
maculata lengi Timb.	Coleoptera	Coccinellidae	ladybeetle	predator	D
Coleophora					
atromarginata Braun	Lepidoptera	Coleophoridae	oak casebearer	oak	C
cerasivorella Pack.	"	"	fruit tree casebearer	fruit trees	C
comptoniella (McD.) (= betulivora McD.)	"	"	lesser birch casebearer	birch	C
laricella (Hbn.)	"	"	larch casebearer	larch	B
laticornella Clem. (= caryaefoliella Clem.)	"	"	pecan cigar casebearer	hickory	C

SCIENTIFIC NAME	ORDER	FAMILY	COMMON NAME	MAIN HOST PLANT(S) OR INSECT TYPE	IMPORTANCE RATING
Coleophora					
malivorella Riley	Lepidoptera	Coleophoridae	pistol casebearer	deciduous	C
ostrayae Clem.	"	"	ironwood casebearer	ironwood	C
pruniella Clem.					
(= *innotabilis* Braun)	"	"	cherry casebearer	deciduous	C
querciella Clem.	"	"	oak casebearer	oak	C
serratella (L.)	"	"	birch casebearer	birch	E
(= *fuscedinella* Zell.)					
tiliaefoliella Clem.	"	"	basswood casebearer	basswood	C
ulmifoliella McD.	"	"	elm casebearer	elm	C
Coleotechnites (= *Eucordylea, Pulicalvaria*)					
apicitripunctella (Clem.)	Lepidoptera	Gelechiidae	green hemlock needle-miner	hemlock	C
(= *abietisella* (Pack.)					
atrupictella (Dietz)	"	"	spruce micro moth	coniferous	C
blastovora (McLeod)	"	"	" "	spruce	C
canusella (Free.)	"	"	banded jack pine needleminer	jack pine	C
carbonarius (Free.)	"	"	juniper needleminer	juniper	C
coniferella (Kft.)	"	"	pine needleminer	pine	C
ducharmei (Free.)	"	"	spruce needleminer	spruce	C
gibsonella (Kft.)	"	"	juniper needleminer	juniper	C
laricis (Free.)	"	"	orange larch tubemaker	larch	C
macleodi (Free.)	"	"	brown hemlock needle-miner	hemlock	C
martini (Free.)	"	"	spruce needleminer	spruce	C
piceaella (Kft.)	"	"	orange spruce needleminer	"	C
resinosae (Free.)	"	"	red pine needleminer	red pine	C
thujaella (Kft.)	"	"	brown cedar leafminer	cedar	B
Collias					
eurytheme Bdv.	Lepidoptera	Pieridae	alfalfa caterpillar	legumes	F
philodice Godt.	"	"	clouded sulphur	"	F
Colocasia					
flavicornis (Sm.)	Lepidoptera	Noctuidae	owlet moth	deciduous	C
propinquilinea (Grt.)	"	"	" "	"	C

SCIENTIFIC NAME	ORDER	FAMILY	COMMON NAME	MAIN HOST PLANT(S) OR INSECT TYPE	IMPORTANCE RATING
Colopha					
ulmicola (Fitch)	Homoptera	Aphididae	elm cockscombgall aphid	elm	C
(Compsolechia) see Anacampsis					
Conophthorus					
banksianae McP.	Coleoptera	Scolytidae	jack pine tip beetle	jack pine	C
coniperda (Schw.)	"	"	white pine cone beetle	white pine	C
resinosae Hopk.	"	"	red pine cone beetle	red pine	C
Conotrachelus					
juglandis LeC.	Coleoptera	Curculionidae	butternut curculio	butternut	C
nenuphar (Hbst.)	"	"	plum curculio	fruit trees	C
Contarinia (See also *Cecidomyia* and *Acericecis*)					
baeri (Prell)	Diptera	Cecidomyiidae	European pine needle midge	Scots and red pines	B
canadensis Felt	"	"	ash midribgall midge	ash	C
negundifolia Felt	"	"	boxelder leafgall midge	Manitoba maple	C
negundinis (Gill.)	"	"	boxelder budgall midge	Manitoba maple	C
virginianiae Felt	"	"	chokecherry midge	chokecherry	C
Coptodisca					
splendoriferella (Clem.)	Lepidoptera	Heliozelidae	resplendent shield bearer	apple	C
Corthylus					
punctatissimus (Zimm.)	Coleoptera	Scolytidae	pitted ambrosia beetle	maple	B

SCIENTIFIC NAME	ORDER	FAMILY	COMMON NAME	MAIN HOST PLANT(S) OR INSECT TYPE	IMPORTANCE RATING
Corythucha					
arcuata (Say)	Hemiptera	Tingidae	oak lace bug	oak	B
associata O. & D.	"	"	birch lace bug	birch	B
ciliata (Say)	"	"	sycamore lace bug	sycamore	C
cydoniae (Fitch)	"	"	hawthorn lace bug	hawthorn	C
elegans Drake	"	"	willow lace bug	willow	B
heidemanni Drake	"	"	alder lace bug	alder	C
juglandis (Fitch)	"	"	walnut lace bug	deciduous	B
mollicula O. & D.	"	"	willow lace bug	willow	C
pallipes Parsh.	"	"	birch lace bug	deciduous	C
pergandei Heid.	"	"	alder lace bug	"	C
ulmi O. & D.	"	"	elm lace bug	elm	B
Cosmia					
calami (Harv.)	Lepidoptera	Noctuidae	owlet moth	oak	C
Cosmopepla					
bimaculata Thos.	Hemiptera	Pentatomidae	twospotted stink bug	predator	D
(Cosymbia) see *Cyclophora*					
Cotalpa					
lanigera (L.)	Coleoptera	Scarabaeidae	goldsmith beetle	poplar	C
Crambidia					
casta (Pack.)	Lepidoptera	Arctiidae	gray footman	unknown	C
pallida Pack.	"	"	pale footman	"	C
Crambus (See also, *Agriphila*, *Catoptria, Chrysoteuchia*)					
agitatellus Clem.	Lepidoptera	Pyralidae	webworm	grasses	F
girardellus Clem.	"	"	"	"	F
hamellus (Thunb.)	"	"	"	"	F
perlellus innotatellus Wlk.	"	"	"	"	F
Crepidodera					
nana (Say)	Coleoptera	Chrysomelidae	tiny aspen flea beetle	aspen	C

SCIENTIFIC NAME	ORDER	FAMILY	COMMON NAME	MAIN HOST PLANT(S) OR INSECT TYPE	IMPORTANCE RATING
(Cressonia) see *Laothoe*					
Crocigrapha					
normani (Grt.)	Lepidoptera	Noctuidae	climbing cherryworm	deciduous	C
Croesia					
curvalana (Kft.)	Lepidoptera	Tortricidae	blueberry leafworm	blueberry	C
semipurpurana (Kft.)	"	"	oak leaf shredder	oak	A
Croesus					
castaneae Roh.	Hymenoptera	Tenthredinidae	chestnut sawfly	chestnut	C
latitarsus Nort.	"	"	dusky birch sawfly	birch	C
Crymodes					
devastator (Brace)	Lepidoptera	Noctuidae	glassy cutworm	sod	F
Cryptocala					
acadiensis (Beth.)	Lepidoptera	Noctuidae	catocaline dart	unknown	C
Cryptocephalus					
notatus F.	Coleoptera	Chrysomelidae	leaf beetle	general feeder	C
quadruplex Newm.	"	"	"	"	C
Cryptococcus					
fagisuga Linding.	Homoptera	Coccidae	beech scale	beech	B
Cryptorhynchus (= *Sternochetus*)					
laptathi (L.)	Coleoptera	Curculionidae	poplar-and-willow borer	poplar, willow	B
Crypturgus					
borealis Swaine	Coleoptera	Scolytidae	bark beetle	coniferous	C
pusillus (Gyll.) (= *atomus* LeC.)	"	"	"	"	C
Ctenicera					
appropinquans Rand.	Coleoptera	Elateridae	click beetle	soil insects	F
arata LeC.	"	"	"	"	F
cruciata pulchra (LeC.)	"	"	"	"	F

SCIENTIFIC NAME	ORDER	FAMILY	COMMON NAME	MAIN HOST PLANT(S) OR INSECT TYPE	IMPORTANCE RATING
Ctenicera					
hieroglyphica (Say)	Coleoptera	Elateridae	click beetle	soil insects	F
kendalli Kby.	"	"	"	"	F
mediana Germ.	"	"	"	"	F
nigricollis Bland	"	"	"	"	F
nitidula LeC.	"	"	"	"	F
ochreipennis (LeC.)	"	"	"	"	F
propola propola (LeC.)	"	"	twospotted click beetle	"	F
resplendens resplendens Esch.	"	"	green click beetle	"	F
spinosa LeC.	"	"	click beetle	"	F
splendens Ziegl.	"	"	"	"	F
triundulata (Rand.)	"	"	threespotted click beetle	"	F
Ctenucha					
virginica (Esp.)	Lepidoptera	Arctiidae	dusky bluebodied moth	grasses	F
Cucullia					
convexipennis G. & R.	Lepidoptera	Noctuidae	aster cutworm	aster, goldenrod flowers	F
intermedia Speyer	"	"	goldenrod cutworm		F
postera Gn.	"	"	aster cutworm	wild aster	F
Culex					
p. pipiens L.	Diptera	Cylicidae	northern house mosquito	biting flies	F
Culicoides spp.	Diptera	Chironomidae	punkie	biting flies	F
Cycloneda					
munda Say	Coleoptera	Coccinellidae	lady beetle	predator	D
Cyclophora					
pendulinaria (Gn.)	Lepidoptera	Geometridae	looper	deciduous	C
Cydia (= *Laspeyresia*)					
candana (Fbs.)	Lepidoptera	Olethreutinae	maple seedworm	maple	C
caryana (Fitch)	"	"	hickory shuckworm	hickory	C
ingrata (Heinr.)	"	"	poplar seedworm	poplar	C
toreuta (Grt.)	"	"	eastern pine seedworm	pine	C
strobilella (L.) (= *youngana* (Kft.))	"	"	spruce seed moth	spruce	B

SCIENTIFIC NAME	ORDER	FAMILY	COMMON NAME	MAIN HOST PLANT(S) OR INSECT TYPE	IMPORTANCE RATING
Cylistix cylindrica Payk.	Coleoptera	Histeridae	hister beetle	predator	D
(Cynips, see *Atrusca)*					
Cyphon variabilis (Thunb.)	Coleoptera	Helodidae	false flower beetle	general feeder	C
Cyrtolobus querci Fitch	Homoptera	Membracidae	treehopper	unknown	C
Cytilus alternatus Say	Coleoptera	Byrrhidae	pill beetle	seedling roots	C
sericeus Forst.	"	"	"	unknown	C
Dahlbominus fuscipennis (Zett.)	Hymenoptera	Eulophidae	chalcid parasite	parasite	D
Danaus plexippus (L.)	Lepidoptera	Danaidae	monarch butterfly	milkweed	F
Darapsa myron (Cram.)	Lepidoptera	Sphingidae	Virginia creeper sphinx	deciduous shrubs	C
pholus (Cram.)	"	"	azalea sphinx		C
Dasineura balsamicola (Lint.)	Diptera	Cecidomyiidae	introduced false balsam gall midge	balsam fir	C
canadensis Felt	"	"	spruce cone gall midge	spruce cones	C
communis Felt	"	"	gouty vein midge	maple	C
gleditschiae O.S.	"	"	honey locust podgall midge	locust	B
rachiphaga Tripp	"	"	spruce cone axis midge	spruce cones	C
serrulatae O.S.	"	"	alder budgall midge	alder	C
Dasychira dorsipennata (B. & McD.)	Lepidoptera	Lymantriidae	hardwood tussock moth	deciduous	C
pinicola (Dyar)	"	"	pine tussock moth	pine	E
plagiata (Wlk.) (= *pini* Dyar)	"	"	northern pine tussock moth	"	C

SCIENTIFIC NAME	ORDER	FAMILY	COMMON NAME	MAIN HOST PLANT(S) OR INSECT TYPE	IMPORTANCE RATING
Dasychira *vagans* (B. & McD.)	Lepidoptera	Lymantriidae	tussock moth	deciduous	C
Dasylophia *thyatiroides* (Wlk.)	Lepidoptera	Notodontidae	beech caterpillar	beech	C
Datana *angusii* G. & R.	Lepidoptera	Notodontidae	striped caterpillar	hickory, butternut	C
contracta Wlk.	"	"	oak caterpillar	oak	C
drexeli Hy. Edw.	"	"	witch hazel caterpillar	witch hazel	C
integerrima G. & R.	"	"	walnut caterpillar	walnut, hickory	B
ministra (Drury)	"	"	yellownecked caterpillar	deciduous	C
perspicua G. & R.	"	"	sumac caterpillar	sumac	C
Delphastus *pusillus* LeC.	Coleoptera	Coccinellidae	lady beetle	predator	D
Dendroctonus *murrayanae* Hopk.	Coleoptera	Scolytidae	lodgepole pine beetle	jack pine, red pine	C
rufipennis (Kby.) (= *obesus* Mann.)	"		spruce beetle	white spruce	C
simplex LeC.	"	"	eastern larch beetle	tamarack	C
valens LeC.	"	"	red turpentine beetle	coniferous	C
Depressaria (see also *Nites*) *pastinacella* (Dup.) (= *heracliana* L.)	Lepidoptera	Oecophoridae	parsnip webworm	umbelliferous	F
Depressariodes (= *Martyrhilda*) *ciniflonella* (Lien. & Zell.) [= *klamathianus* (Wlsm.)]	Lepidoptera	Oecophoridae	leafroller	poplar, alder	C
Dermestes *lardarius* L.	Coleoptera	Dermestidae	larder beetle	household pest	G
Desmia *funeralis* (Hbn.)	Lepidoptera	Pyralidae	grape leaffolder	vines	F

SCIENTIFIC NAME	ORDER	FAMILY	COMMON NAME	MAIN HOST PLANT(S) OR INSECT TYPE	IMPORTANCE RATING
(*Deuteronomos*) see *Ennomos*					
Diachrysia balluca Gey.	Lepidoptera	Noctuidae	false looper	raspberry	F
Diachus catarius Suffr.	Coleoptera	Chrysomelidae	leaf beetle	willow	C
Diapheromera femorata (Say)	Orthoptera	Phasmatidae	walking stick	deciduous	B
Diarsia jucunda (Wlk.)	Lepidoptera	Noctuidae	smaller pinkish dart	unknown	C
Dicerca divaricata (Say)	Coleoptera	Buprestidae	flatheaded hardwood borer	dead trees	C
tenebrica (Kby.)	"	"	flatheaded poplar borer	"	C
tenebrosa (Kby.)	"	"	flatheaded conifer borer	"	C
Dichelonyx albicollis (Burm.)	Coleoptera	Scarabaeidae	leaf chafer	deciduous	C
backi (Kby.)	"	"	green rose chafer	"	C
elongatula (Schonh.)	"	"	leaf chafer	"	C
linearis (Gyll.)	"	"	"	"	C
subvittata LeC.	"	"	"	"	C
Dichomeris ligulella Hbn.	Lepidoptera	Gelechiidae	Palmerworm	deciduous	C
marginella (F.)	"	"	juniper webworm	juniper	C
Dicrodiplosis populi Felt	Diptera	Cecidomyiidae	poplar leafgall midge	poplar	C
Dictyopterus aurora Hbst.	Coleoptera	Lycidae	netwinged beetle	decaying wood	C
Dimorphopteryx melanognathus Roh.	Hymenoptera	Tenthredinidae	fringed birch sawfly	birch, alder	B

SCIENTIFIC NAME	ORDER	FAMILY	COMMON NAME	MAIN HOST PLANT(S) OR INSECT TYPE	IMPORTANCE RATING
Dioryctria					
abietivorella (Grt.)	Lepidoptera	Pyralidae	fir coneworm	coniferous	C
disclusa Heinr.	"	"	webbing coneworm	pine cone	C
reniculelloides Mut. & Mun.	"	"	spruce coneworm	spruce, balsam fir	C
resinosella Mut.	"	"	red pine shoot moth	red pine	C
zimmermani (Grt.)	"	"	Zimmerman pine moth	pine	C
Diplolepis					
rosae (L.)	Hymenoptera	Cynipidae	mossy rose gall wasp	rose	C
Diprion					
similis (Htg.)	Hymenoptera	Diprionidae	introduced pine sawfly	pine	C
Disonycha					
alternata (Ill.)	Coleoptera	Chrysomelidae	striped willow leaf beetle	willow	C
Drepana					
arcuata Wlk.	Lepidoptera	Drepanidae	masked birch caterpillar	birch, alder	C
bilineata (Pack.)	"	"	warty birch caterpillar	birch	C
Dryocampa					
rubicunda (F.)	Lepidoptera	Citheroniidae	greenstriped mapleworm	maple	A
rubicunda alba Grt.	"	"	"	"	A
Dryocoetes					
affaber (Mann.)	Coleoptera	Scoytidae	bark beetle	spruce, pine	C
autographus (Ratz.)	"	"	"	coniferous	C
betulae Hopk.	"	"	birch bark beetle	white birch	C
Dryocosmus					
deciduus (Beut.)	Hymenoptera	Cynipidae	oak gall wasp	oak	C
quercuspalustris (O. S.)	"	"	"	"	C
Dyspteris					
abortivaria (H.-S.)	Lepidoptera	Geometridae	green grape-geometer	grape	C

SCIENTIFIC NAME	ORDER	FAMILY	COMMON NAME	MAIN HOST PLANT(S) OR INSECT TYPE	IMPORTANCE RATING
Dysstroma					
citrata (L.)	Lepidoptera	Geometridae	dark marbled carpet	general feeder	C
truncata Hufn.	"	"	looper	"	C
Eacles					
imperialis pini Mich.	Lepidoptera	Citheroniidae	pine imperial moth	pine	C
Ecdytolopha					
insiticiana Zell.	Lepidoptera	Olethreutinae	locust twig borer	locust	C
punctidiscana (Dyar)	"	"	micro moth	"	C
Ecpantheria					
scribonia (Stoll)	Lepidoptera	Arctiidae	great leopard moth	unknown	C
Ectoedemia					
argyropeza downesi W. & S.	Lepidoptera	Nepticulidae	aspen petiole miner	aspen	C
canutus W. & S.	"	"	balsam poplar petiole miner	balsam poplar	C
lindquisti (Free.)	"	"	small birch leafminer	birch	C
populella Bsk.	"	"	poplar petiolegall moth	poplar	C
Ectropis					
crepuscularia (D. & S.)	Lepidoptera	Geometridae	saddleback looper	general feeder	C
Egira (= *Xylomyges*)					
dolosa Grt.	Lepidoptera	Noctuidae	lined black aspen caterpillar	aspen	C
Eilema					
bicolor (Grt.)	Lepidoptera	Arctiidae	smoky moth	coniferous	C
Eitelius					
gregarius (Marl.)	Hymenoptera	Tenthredinidae	willow skeletonizing sawfly	willow	C
Elaphidionoides					
parallelus (Newm.)	Coleoptera	Cerambycidae	hickory twig pruner	oak, hickory	C
villosus (F.)	"	"	twig pruner	red oak	C

SCIENTIFIC NAME	ORDER	FAMILY	COMMON NAME	MAIN HOST PLANT(S) OR INSECT TYPE	IMPORTANCE RATING
Elaphria festivoides (Gn.)	Lepidoptera	Noctuidae	owlet moth	general feeder	C
versicolor (Grt.)	"	"	fir harlequin	"	C
Elasmostethus cruciatus Say	Hemiptera	Pentatomidae	redcrossed stink bug	unknown	C
Ellida caniplaga (Wlk.)	Lepidoptera	Notodontidae	basswood caterpillar	basswood	C
Ematurga amitaria (Gn.)	Lepidoptera	Geometridae	cranberry spanworm	deciduous	C
Empoasca fabae (Harr.)	Homoptera	Cicadellidae	potato leafhopper	deciduous	C
Empria multicolor (Nort.)	Hymenoptera	Tenthredinidae	sawfly	white birch, alder	C
Enargia decolor (Wlk.)	Lepidoptera	Noctuidae	aspen twoleaf tier	poplar	B
infumata (Grt.)	"	"	owlet moth	birch	C
Enchenopa binotata (Say)	Homoptera	Membracidae	twomarked treehopper	deciduous	C
Endopiza piceana (Free.)	Lepidoptera	Olethreutinae	spruce micro moth	spruce	C
Endothenia albolineana (Kft.)	Lepidoptera	Olethreutinae	spruce needleminer	"	C
Ennomos (= Deuteronomos) magnaria Gn.	Lepidoptera	Geometridae	maple spanworm, or notchwing geometer	deciduous	C
subsignaria (Hbn.)	"	"	elm spanworm	elm	B

SCIENTIFIC NAME	ORDER	FAMILY	COMMON NAME	MAIN HOST PLANT(S) OR INSECT TYPE	IMPORTANCE RATING
Enodia					
anthedon borealis Clark (= *portlandia borealis*)	Lepidoptera	Satyridae	pearly eye	grass	F
Epargyreus					
clarus (Cram.)	Lepidoptera	Hesperiidae	silverspotted skipper	locust	C
Ephestia					
elutella (Hbn.)	Lepidoptera	Pyralidae	tobacco moth	household pest	C
Epiblema					
resamptana (Wlk.)	Lepidoptera	Olethreutinae	micro moth	unknown	C
Epicauta					
fabricii (LeC.)	Coleoptera	Meloidae	ashgray blister beetle	unknown	C
murina LeC.	"	"	dark blister beetle	deciduous	C
(*Epicnaptera*) see *Phyllodesma*					
Epiglaea					
apiata (Grt.)	Lepidoptera	Noctuidae	owlet moth	cranberry, blueberry	C
Epinotia					
aceriella (Clem.)	Lepidoptera	Olethreutinae	maple trumpet skeletonizer	maple	C
albanguiana (Wlsm.)	"	"	alder leafroller	alder	C
corylana McD.	"	"	alder catkin moth	"	C
crenana (Hbn.)	"	"	willow leafroller	willow	C
criddleana (Kft.)	"	"	aspen leafroller	poplar	C
cruciana (L.)	"	"	willow leaftier	willow	C
lindana (Fern.)	"	"	dogwood leafroller	dogwood	C
medioplagata (Wlsm.)	"	"	willow leafroller	willow	C
momonana (Kft.)	"	"	alder budminer	alder	C
nanana (Treit.)	"	"	European spruce needleminer	spruce	C
nigralbana (Wlsm.)	"	"	micro moth	alder	C
nisella (Cl.)	"	"	yellowheaded aspen leaftier	aspen	C
normanana Kft.	"	"	spruce needleminer	spruce	C

SCIENTIFIC NAME	ORDER	FAMILY	COMMON NAME	MAIN HOST PLANT(S) OR INSECT TYPE	IMPORTANCE RATING
Epinotia					
rectiplicana (Wlsm.)	Lepidoptera	Olethreutinae	micro moth	deciduous	C
septemberana Kft.	"	"	"	Labrador tea	C
solandriana (L.)	"	"	birch-aspen leafroller	birch, poplar	B
solicitana (Wlk.)	"	"	birch shootworm	birch	C
timidella (Clem.)	"	"	oak trumpet skeletonizer	oak	C
transmissana (Wlk.)	"	"	birch catkin moth	birch	C
Epirrita					
autumnata henshawi (Swett)	Lepidoptera	Olethreutinae	November moth	larch	C
Episimus					
argutanus (Clem.)	Lepidoptera	Olethreutinae	sumac leafroller	sumac	C
(*Epizeuxis*) see *Idia*					
Erannis					
tiliaria (Harr.)	Lepidoptera	Geometridae	linden looper	deciduous	B
Eriocampa					
juglandis (Fitch)	Hymenoptera	Tenthredinidae	woolly butternut sawfly	butternut, walnut	C
ovata (L.)	"	"	woolly alder sawfly	alder	C
Eriophyes (see also *Aceria* and *Phytocoptella*)					
betulae (Nal.)	Acari	Eriophyidae	birch "witches broom" mite	birch	C
fraxiniflora (Felt)	"	"	ash flowergall mite	ash	C
negundi Hodg.	"	"	Manitoba maple gall mite	Manitoba maple	C
populi Nal.	"	"	poplar gall mite	poplar	C
semen Walsh.	"	"	willow leafgall mite	willow	C
Eriosoma					
americanum (Riley)	Homoptera	Aphididae	woolly elm aphid	elm	C
crataegi (Oestl.)	"	"	woolly hawthorn aphid	hawthorn	C
lanigerum (Hausm.)	"	"	woolly apple aphid	elm, apple	C

SCIENTIFIC NAME	ORDER	FAMILY	COMMON NAME	MAIN HOST PLANT(S) OR INSECT TYPE	IMPORTANCE RATING
Erynnis					
icelus (Scudd. & Burg.)	Lepidoptera	Hesperiidae	dreamy dusky wing	poplar, willow	C
juvenalis (Fabr.)	"	"	Juvenal's dusky wing	oak	C
Estigmene (see also *Spilosoma*)					
acrea (Drury)	Lepidoptera	Arctiidae	saltmarsh caterpillar	grasses	F
Euceraphis					
betulae (Koch.)	Homoptera	Aphididae	birch aphid	birch	C
punctipennis (Zett.)	"	"	European birch aphid	"	C
Euchaetes					
egle (Drury)	Lepidoptera	Arctiidae	milkweed tussock	milkweed	F
Euchlaena					
effecta (Wlk.)	Lepidoptera	Geometridae	looper	deciduous	C
irraria (B. & McD.)	"	"	"	aspen	C
johnsonaria (Fitch)	"	"	"	deciduous	C
madusaria (Wlk.)	"	"	"	jack pine	C
marginaria (Minot)	"	"	"	deciduous	C
tigrinaria (Gn.)	"	"	"	"	C
Eucirroedia					
pampina (Gn.)	Lepidoptera	Noctuidae	owlet moth	deciduous	C
Euclea					
delphinii (Bdv.)	Lepidoptera	Limacodidae	spiny slug caterpillar	deciduous	C
Euclidia					
cuspidea (Hbn.)	Lepidoptera	Noctuidae	owlet moth	clover	F
(*Eucordylea*) see *Coleotechnites*					
Eucosma					
gloriola Heinr.	Lepidoptera	Olethreutinae	eastern pine shoot borer	pine	B
monitorana Heinr.	"	"	red pine cone borer	red pine	C
tocullionana Heinr.	"	"	white pine cone borer	pine	C

SCIENTIFIC NAME	ORDER	FAMILY	COMMON NAME	MAIN HOST PLANT(S) OR INSECT TYPE	IMPORTANCE RATING
Eudeilinia herminiata (Gn.)	Lepidoptera	Drepanidae	dogwood caterpillar	dogwood	C
Eudryas (= Euthisanotia) grata (F.)	Lepidoptera	Noctuidae	beautiful wood nymph	vines	F
unio (Hbn.)	"	"	pearly wood nymph	ground plants	F
Eueretagrotis attenta (Grt.)	Lepidoptera	Noctuidae	cutworm	unknown	C
perattenta (Grt.)	"	"	"	"	C
Eufidonia discospilata (Wlk.)	Lepidoptera	Geometridae	looper	coniferous	C
notataria (Wlk.)	"	"	conifer looper	"	C
Eugonobapta nivosaria (Gn.)	Lepidoptera	Geometridae	looper	maple	C
Eulachnus (= Protolachnus) agilis (Kltb.)	Homoptera	Aphididae	spotted black pine needle aphid	pine	C
rileyi (Wlms.)	"	"	powdery pine needle aphid	"	C
Eulithis (= Lygris) diversilineata (Hbn.)	Lepidoptera	Geometridae	grapevine looper	grapevine	F
Eumacaria (= Itame in part) *latiferrugata* (Wlk.)	Lepidoptera	Geometridae	cherry spanworm	cherry	C
Eumorpha achemon (Drury)	Lepidoptera	Sphingidae	achemon sphinx	virginia creeper	F
Eupareophora parca (Cress.) (= *minuta* MacG.)	Hymenoptera	Tenthredinidae	spiny ash sawfly	ash	C
Euparthenos nubilis (Hbn.)	Lepidoptera	Geometridae	locust caterpillar, or underwing	locust	C

SCIENTIFIC NAME	ORDER	FAMILY	COMMON NAME	MAIN HOST PLANT(S) OR INSECT TYPE	IMPORTANCE RATING
Euphoria					
fulgida F.	Coleoptera	Scarabaeidae	scarab beetle	decayed wood	F
inda (L.)	"	"	bumble flower beetle	"	F
Eupithecia					
albicapitata Pack.	Lepidoptera	Geometridae	spruce cone geometer	spruce, balsam fir	C
annulata (Hlst.)	"	"	conifer looper	coniferous	C
coagulata Gn.	"	"	looper	ground plants	F
filmata Pears.	"	"	early brown looper	coniferous	C
fletcherata Tayl.	"	"	looper	"	C
gelidata Mosch.	"	"	"	birch	C
gibsonata Tayl.	"	"	conifer looper	coniferous	C
intricata (Zett.)	"	"	juniper looper	juniper	C
luteata Pack.	"	"	fir needle inchworm	coniferous	C
misturata frostiata Swett	"	"	tamarack looper	tamarack	C
mutata Pears.	"	"	spruce cone looper	spruce, balsam fir	C
palpata Pack.	"	"	small pine looper	pine	C
pusillata interruptofasciata Pack.	"	"	juniper looper	juniper	C
ravocostaliata Pack.	"	"	looper	deciduous	C
sheppardata McD.	"	"	alder looper	alder	C
strattonata Pack.	"	"	spirea looper	spiraea	C
subfuscata (Haw.)	"	"	looper	coniferous	C
transcanadata MacK.	"	"	small conifer looper	"	C
Euplexia					
benesimilis McD.	Lepidoptera	Noctuidae	owlet moth	general feeder	C
Euproctis					
chrysorrhoea (L.)	Lepidoptera	Lymantriidae	browntail moth	deciduous	E
Eupsilia					
morrisoni (Grt.)	Lepidoptera	Noctuidae	owlet moth	elm, maple	C
tristigmata (Grt.)	"	"	"	cherry	C
Euptoieta					
claudia (Cram.)	Lepidoptera	Nymphalidae	variegated fritillary	ground plant	F
Eurois					
astricta Morr.	Lepidoptera	Noctuidae	cutworm	poplar	C
occulta (L.)	"	"	"	general feeder	C

SCIENTIFIC NAME	ORDER	FAMILY	COMMON NAME	MAIN HOST PLANT(S) OR INSECT TYPE	IMPORTANCE RATING
Eurrhypara hortulata (L.)	Lepidoptera	Pyralidae	nettle micro moth	nettle	F
Euschistus euschistoides Voll.	Hemiptera	Pentatomidae	stink bug	general feeder	C
tristigmus (Say)	"	"	dusky stink bug	"	C
(Euthisanotia) see *Eudryas*					
Euthyatira pudens (Gn.)	Lepidoptera	Thyatiridae	false owlet moth	dogwood	C
Eutrapela clemataria (J.E. Smith)	Lepidoptera	Geometridae	purplish-brown looper	general feeder	C
Euura atra (Jur.)	Hymenoptera	Tenthredinidae	smaller willowshoot sawfly	willow	C
s-nodus Walsh	"	"	willow twig-gall sawfly	"	C
Euxoa messoria (Harr.)	Lepidoptera	Noctuidae	darksided cutworm	maple seedlings (agricultural pest)	C
ochrogaster (Gn.)	"	"	redbacked cutworm	agricultural pest	F
scandens (Riley)	"	"	white cutworm	"	C
tessellata (Harr.)	"	"	striped cutworm	"	C
Evodinus monticola (Rand.)	Coleoptera	Cerambycidae	longhorned beetle	hemlock	C
Evora hemidesma (Zell.)	Lepidoptera	Olethreutinae	spirea leaftier	deciduous	C
(Exartema) see *Olethreutes*					
Exochomus septentrionis Weise	Coleoptera	Coccinellidae	lady beetle	predator	D

SCIENTIFIC NAME	ORDER	FAMILY	COMMON NAME	MAIN HOST PLANT(S) OR INSECT TYPE	IMPORTANCE RATING
Exoteleia					
dodecella (L.)	Lepidoptera	Gelechiidae	pine bud moth	pine	B
nepheos Free.	"	"	pine candle moth	"	C
pinifoliella (Cham.)	"	"	pine needleminer	jack pine	B
Fagiphagus					
imbricator (Fitch)	Homoptera	Aphididae	beech blight aphid	beech	C
Feltia					
herilis (Grt.)	Lepidoptera	Noctuidae	dingy cutworm	unknown	C
Feniseca					
tarquinius (F.)	Lepidoptera	Lycaenidae	harvester	predator	D
Fenusa					
dohrnii (Tisch.)	Hymenoptera	Tenthredinidae	European alder leafminer	alder	B
pusilla (Lep.)	"	"	birch leafminer	birch	A
ulmi Sund.	"	"	elm leafminer	elm	B
Feralia					
comstocki (Grt.)	Lepidoptera	Noctuidae	redlined conifer caterpillar	coniferous	C
jocosa (Gn.)	"	"	redlined conifer caterpillar, joker	"	C
major Sm.	"	"	redlined conifer caterpillar	spruce, pine	C
Filatima					
betulae Clarke	Lepidoptera	Gelechiidae	birch leafroller	birch	C
demissae (Keif.)	"	"	leafroller	serviceberry	C
Forficula					
auricularia L.	Dermaptera	Forficulidae	European earwig	ground plants	F
Framinghamia					
helvalis (Wlk.)	Lepidoptera	Pyralidae	poplar leafroller	poplar	C
(*Fumea*) see *Psyche*					

SCIENTIFIC NAME	ORDER	FAMILY	COMMON NAME	MAIN HOST PLANT(S) OR INSECT TYPE	IMPORTANCE RATING
Furcula (See also *Cerura*)					
borealis (G. -M.)	Lepidoptera	Notodontidae	forktailed caterpillar	deciduous	C
cinerea (Wlk.)	"	"	"	willow	C
modesta (Hud.)	"	"	"	"	C
occidentalis (Lint.)	"	"	"	willow, poplar	C
scolopendrina (Bdv.)	"	"	"	deciduous	C
(*Galerucella*) see *Pyrrhalta*					
Gargaphia tiliae (Walsh)	Hemiptera	Tingidae	basswood lace bug	basswood	C
Gastrophysa cyanea (Melsh.)	Coleoptera	Chrysomelidae	leaf beetle	dock, rhubarb	F
Geina periscelidactyla (Fitch)	Lepidoptera	Pterophoridae	grape plume moth	grapevine	C
Gelechia versutella Zell.	Lepidoptera	Gelechiidae	poplar micro moth	aspen	C
Geotrupes balyi Jekel	Coleoptera	Scarabaeidae	scarab beetle	scavenger	F
Gilpinia frutetorum (F.)	Hymenoptera	Diprionidae	nursery pine sawfly	pine	C
hercyniae (Htg.)	"	"	European spruce sawfly	spruce	C
Glischrochilus quadrisignatus (Say)	Coleoptera	Nitidulidae	fourspotted sap beetle	sap of plants	C
sanguinolentus Oliv.	"	"	sap beetle	"	C
Gluphisia avimacula Hud.	Lepidoptera	Notodontidae	poplar caterpillar	poplar	C
lintneri (Grt.)	"	"	"	"	C
septentrionalis Wlk.	"	"	pale green notodontid	deciduous	C

SCIENTIFIC NAME	ORDER	FAMILY	COMMON NAME	MAIN HOST PLANT(S) OR INSECT TYPE	IMPORTANCE RATING
Glycobius speciosus (Say)	Coleoptera	Cerambycidae	sugar maple borer	maple	C
Glyphipteryx linneella (Clk.)	Lepidoptera	Cosmopterygidae	linden bark borer	European linden	C
Glypta fumiferanae (Vier.)	Hymenoptera	Ichneumonidae	parasite	budworms	D
Glyptoscelis pubescens (F.)	Coleoptera	Chrysomelidae	hairy leaf beetle	general feeder	C
Gnophothrips fuscus (Morgan) (= *piniphilis* Cwfd.)	Thysanoptera	Phloeothripidae	slash pine flower thrips	pine	C
Gobaishia ulmifusus (W. & R.)	Homoptera	Aphididae	elm pouchgall aphid	elm	C
Gonioctena americana (Schaeff.) *notmani* (Schaeff.)	Coleoptera "	Chrysomelidae "	American aspen beetle willow leaf beetle	poplar willow	B C
Gossyparia spuria (Mod.)	Homoptera	Coccidae	European elm scale	elm	C
(*Gracillaria*) see *Caloptilia*					
Grammoptera subargentata (Kby.)	Coleoptera	Cerambycidae	longhorned beetle	deciduous	C
Graphiphora haruspica (Grt.)	Lepidoptera	Noctuidae	cutworm	willow, birch	C
Graphocephala coccinea (Forst.)	Homoptera	Cicadellidae	leafhopper	shrubs	C
Grapholita prunivora (Walsh)	Lepidoptera	Olethreutinae	lesser appleworm	apple	C

SCIENTIFIC NAME	ORDER	FAMILY	COMMON NAME	MAIN HOST PLANT(S) OR INSECT TYPE	IMPORTANCE RATING
Gretchena					
amatana Heinr.	Lepidoptera	Olethreutinae	micro moth	walnut, butternut	C
delicatana Heinr.	"	"	ironwood fruitworm	ironwood	C
semialba McD.	"	"	alder leaftier	alder	C
Griselda					
radicana Heinr.	Lepidoptera	Olethreutinae	redstriped needleworm	spruce	C
Gypsonoma					
fasciolana Clem.	Lepidoptera	Olethreutinae	willow-and-poplar leafroller	willow, poplar	C
haimbachiana Kft.	"	"	cottonwood twig borer	poplar	C
salicicolana Clem.	"	"	willow leafroller	willow	C
substitutionis Heinr.	"	"	micro moth	deciduous	C
Habrosyne					
scripta (Gosse)	Lepidoptera	Thyatiridae	false owlet moth	unknown	C
Halysidota (see also *Lophocampa*)					
harrisii Walsh.	Lepidoptera	Arctiidae	sycamore tussock moth	sycamore	C
tessellaris (J.E. Smith)	"	"	pale tussock moth	deciduous	C
Hamamelistes					
spinosis Shimer	Homoptera	Aphididae	witch hazel gall aphid	hazel	C
Haploa					
confusa (Lyman)	Lepidoptera	Arctiidae	Lyman's haploa	deciduous	C
contigua (Wlk.)	"	"	tiger moth	aspen	C
lecontei (G.-M.)	"	"	LeConte's haploa	deciduous	C
Hedya					
chionosema (Zell.)	Lepidoptera	Olethreutinae	micro moth	deciduous	C
ochroleucana (Froh.)	"	"	rose leafroller	"	C
separatana (Kft.)	"	"	micro moth	birch, serviceberry	C
(*Helicoverpa*) see *Heliothis*					
Heliomata					
cycladata G. and R.	Lepidoptera	Geometridae	stout locust looper	locust	C

SCIENTIFIC NAME	ORDER	FAMILY	COMMON NAME	MAIN HOST PLANT(S) OR INSECT TYPE	IMPORTANCE RATING
Heliothis zea (Boddie)	Lepidoptera	Noctuidae	corn earworm or tomato fruitworm or bollworm	corn, tomato	G
Helotropha reniformis (Grt.)	Lepidoptera	Geometridae	owlet moth	unknown	C
Hemaris diffinis (Bdv.)	Lepidoptera	Sphingidae	snowberry clearwing	deciduous	C
gracilis (G. & R.)	"	"	clearwing hawk moth	"	C
thysbe (F.)	"	"	hummingbird clearwing	"	C
Hemichroa crocea (Geoff.)	Hymenoptera	Tenthredinidae	striped alder sawfly	alder	C
militaris (Cress.)	"	"	cherry sawfly	cherry	C
Hepialus gracilis Grt.	Lepidoptera	Hepialidae	graceful ghost moth	unknown	C
Heptagrotis phyllophora (Grt.)	Lepidoptera	Noctuidae	cutworm	deciduous	C
Herculia thymetusalis (Wlk.)	Lepidoptera	Pyralidae	spruce micro moth	spruce	C
intermedialis (Wlk.)	"	"	conifer micro moth	spruce, balsam fir	C
Herpetogramma pertextalis (Led.)	Lepidoptera	Pyralidae	leafroller	deciduous	C
thestialis (Wlk.)	"	"	"	"	C
Hesperia sassacus Harr.	Lepidoptera	Hesperiidae	Indian skipper	unknown	C
Hesperumia sulphuraria Pack.	Lepidoptera	Geometridae	looper	general feeder	C
Heterarthrus nemoratus (Fall.)	Hymenoptera	Tenthredinidae	late birchleaf edgeminer	birch	C

SCIENTIFIC NAME	ORDER	FAMILY	COMMON NAME	MAIN HOST PLANT(S) OR INSECT TYPE	IMPORTANCE RATING
Heterocampa (see also *Lochmaeus*)					
biundata Wlk.	Lepidoptera	Notodontidae	prominent moth	deciduous	C
guttivitta (Wlk.)	"	"	saddled prominent	sugar maple, beech	A
obliqua Pack.	"	"	prominent moth	oak	C
umbrata Wlk.	"	"	"	birch, oak	C
umbrata pulverea G. & R.	"	"	"	"	C
Heterophleps					
refusaria (Wlk.)	Lepidoptera	Geometridae	looper	unknown	C
triguttaria H.-S.	"	"	"	maple	C
Hethemia					
pistasciaria (Gn.)	Lepidoptera	Geometridae	looper	deciduous	C
Hippodamia					
convergens G.-M.	Coleoptera	Coccinellidae	convergent lady beetle	predator	D
parenthesis Say	"	"	lady beetle	"	D
tredecimpunctata tibialis (Say)	"	"	thirteenspotted lady beetle	"	D
Holcocera					
chalcofrontella Clem.	Lepidoptera	Blastobasidae	sumac micro moth	sumac	C
Holcocerina					
immaculella (McD.)	Lepidoptera	Blastobasidae	conifer micro moth	pine, spruce	C
Holomelina					
aurantiaca (Hbn.)	Lepidoptera	Arctiidae	arctiid moth	pine	C
ferruginosa (Wlk.)	"	"	"	unknown	C
laeta treatii (Grt.)	"	"	"	"	C
Homadaula					
anisocentra Meyr.	Lepidoptera	Glyphipterygidae	mimosa webworm	locust	B
Homoglaea					
hircina Morr.	Lepidoptera	Noctuidae	goat sallow	aspen	C

SCIENTIFIC NAME	ORDER	FAMILY	COMMON NAME	MAIN HOST PLANT(S) OR INSECT TYPE	IMPORTANCE RATING
Homohadena badistriga (Grt.)	Lepidoptera	Noctuidae	honeysuckle budworm	honeysuckle	C
Hoplia trifasciata Say	Coleoptera	Scarabaeidae	scarab beetle	flowers	F
Hoplochaitophorus quercicola Monell	Homoptera	Aphididae	oak aphid	oak	C
Horisme intestinata (Gn.)	Lepidoptera	Geometridae	looper	unknown	C
Hormaphis hamamelidis (Fitch)	Homoptera	Aphididae	witch-hazel conegall aphid	witch-hazel	C
Hyalophora cecropia (L.) *columbia* Smith	Lepidoptera "	Saturniidae "	cecropia moth / larch silkworm or columbian silkmoth	deciduous / larch	C / C
Hybomitra zonalis (Kby.)	Diptera	Tabanidae	moose fly	biting insect	F
Hydrelia inornata (Hlst.)	Lepidoptera	Geometridae	birch looper	birch	C
Hydria prunivorata (Fgn.)	Lepidoptera	Geometridae	cherry scallopshell moth	black cherry	B
undulata (L.)	"	"	scallopshell moth	deciduous	C
Hydriomena divisaria (Wlk.)	Lepidoptera	Geometridae	transverse banded looper	spruce	C
furcata (Thunb.)	"	"	transverse banded looper	willow, ash	C
renunciata (Wlk.)	"	"	alder looper	alder	C

SCIENTIFIC NAME	ORDER	FAMILY	COMMON NAME	MAIN HOST PLANT(S) OR INSECT TYPE	IMPORTANCE RATING
Hylastes porculus Er.	Coleoptera	Scolytidae	bark beetle	pine	C
(Hylemya) see *Lasiomma*					
Hyles gallii (Rott.)	Lepidoptera	Sphingidae	bedstraw sphinx	ground plants	F
Hylobius congener D.T.	Coleoptera	Curculionidae	bark weevil	pine logs or stumps	C
pales (Hbst.)	"	"	pales weevil	pine	B
piceus (DeG.)	"	"	large spruce weevil	spruce	C
pinicola (Couper)	"	"	Couper's collar weevil	pine	C
radicis Buch.	"	"	pine root collar weevil	"	B
warreni Wood	"	"	Warren's root collar weevil	coniferous	C
Hylurgopinus rufipes (Eich.)	Coleoptera	Scolytidae	native elm bark beetle	elm	A
Hylurgops pinifex (Fitch)	Coleoptera	Scolytidae	bark beetle	pine, spruce	C
Hymenorus discretus Casey	Coleoptera	Alleculidae	combclawed beetle	deciduous	C
melsheimeri Casey	"	"	"	"	C
niger Melsh.	"	"	"	"	C
pilosus Melsh.	"	"	"	"	C
Hypagyrtis piniata (Pack.)	Lepidoptera	Geometridae	diamond backed conifer looper	coniferous	C
unipunctata (Haw.) (= *subatomaria* (Wood))	"	"	onespotted variant	deciduous	C
Hypera punctata (F.)	Coleoptera	Curculionidae	clover leaf weevil	clover	F

SCIENTIFIC NAME	ORDER	FAMILY	COMMON NAME	MAIN HOST PLANT(S) OR INSECT TYPE	IMPORTANCE RATING
Hyperaspis					
bigeminata (Rand.)	Coleoptera	Coccinellidae	lady beetle	predator	D
binotata (Say)	"	"	"	"	D
congressis Watson	"	"	"	"	D
paspalis Watson	"	"	"	"	D
proba (Say)	"	"	"	"	D
(Hyperetis) see *Probole*					
Hyperstrotia					
pervertens (B. & McD.)	Lepidoptera	Noctuidae	owlet moth	elm, oak	C
Hyphantria					
cunea (Drury)	Lepidoptera	Arctiidae	fall webworm	deciduous	B
Hypoprepia					
fucosa Hbn.	Lepidoptera	Arctiidae	painted lichen moth	general feeder	C
miniata (Kby.)	"	"	scarletwinged lichen moth	"	C
Hyposoter					
fugitivus fugitivus (Say)	Hymenoptera	Ichneumonidae	parasite	parasite	D
Hyppa					
xylinoides (Gn.)	Lepidoptera	Noctuidae	cranberry cutworm	cranberry	C
Hysterosia (= *Phalonia*)					
albidana Wlk.	Lepidoptera	Cochylidae	micro moth	deciduous	C
straminoides Grt.	"	"	basswood seed moth	basswood	C
(Ichthyura) see *Clostera*					
Idia (= *Epizeuxis*)					
aemula Hbn.	Lepidoptera	Noctuidae	owlet moth	spruce	C
americalis (Gn.)	"	"	"	"	C
lubricalis (Gey.)	"	"	"	unknown	C
Idiocerus					
populi L.	Homoptera	Cicadellidae	leafhopper	poplar	C

SCIENTIFIC NAME	ORDER	FAMILY	COMMON NAME	MAIN HOST PLANT(S) OR INSECT TYPE	IMPORTANCE RATING
Incisalia (= *Callophrys*) *niphon clarki* Free.	Lepidoptera	Lycaenidae	pine elfin	pine, spruce	C
Ipimorpha pleonectusa Grt.	Lepidoptera	Noctuidae	blackcheeked aspen caterpillar	poplar, willow	C
Ips					
borealis Sw.	Coleoptera	Scolytidae	northern engraver	spruce	C
calligraphus (Germ.)	"	"	coarsewriting engraver	pine	C
grandicollis (Eich.)	"	"	southern pine engraver	"	C
perroti Sw.	"	"	pine engraver	"	C
perturbatus (Eich.)	"	"	northern spruce engraver	spruce	C
pini (Say)	"	"	pine engraver	pine, spruce	B
Iridopsis larvaria (Gn.)	Lepidoptera	Geometridae	looper	deciduous	C
Isa textula (H.-S.)	Lepidoptera	Limacodidae	slug caterpillar	white oak	C
(*Isia*) see *Pyrrharctia*					
Isomira quadristriata Couper	Coleoptera	Alleculidae	combclawed beetle	deciduous	C
Itame (see also *Eumacaria*)					
anataria (Swett)	Lepidoptera	Geometridae	spanworm	white birch	C
argillacearia (Pack.)	"	"	"	pine	C
brunneata (Thunb.) (= *fulvaria* (Vill.))	"	"	"	spruce	C
exauspicata (Wlk.)	"	"	"	deciduous	C
loricaria julia (Hlst.)	"	"	false Bruce spanworm	aspen, poplar	C
pustularia (Gn.)	"	"	lesser maple spanworm	maple	C
ribearia (Fitch)	"	"	currant spanworm	currant	C
Itonida canadensis Feltham	Diptera	Cecidomyiidae	juneberry veingall midge	juneberry	C

SCIENTIFIC NAME	ORDER	FAMILY	COMMON NAME	MAIN HOST PLANT(S) OR INSECT TYPE	IMPORTANCE RATING
Itoplectis *conquisitor* (Say)	Hymenoptera	Ichneumonidae	parasite	parasite	D
Janus *abbreviatus* (Say)	Hymenoptera	Cephidae	willow shoot sawfly	willow, poplar	C
integer (Nort.)	"	"	currant stem girdler	currant	C
Japanogromyza *viridula* (Ooq.)	Diptera	Agromyzidae	leafminer	white oak	C
Kleidocerys *resedae geminatus* (Say)	Hemiptera	Lygaeidae	birch catkin bug	birch	C
Labidomera *clivicollis* (Kby.)	Coleoptera	Chrysomelidae	milkweed leaf beetle	milkweed	F
Lacanobia (see also *Melanchra, Papestra, Polia*)					
grandis (Gn.)	Lepidoptera	Noctuidae	cutworm	willow, cherry	C
legitima (Grt.)	"	"	striped garden caterpillar	general feeder	C
lilacina (Harv.)	"	"	flax cutworm	field crops	G
lutra (Gn.)	"	"	cutworm	general feeder	C
nevadae (Grt.)	"	"	"	birch	C
radix (Wlk.)	"	"	"	birch, alder	C
tacoma (Stkr.)	"	"	"	cherry, birch	C
Lacinipolia *lorea* (Gn.)	Lepidoptera	Noctuidae	cutworm	dandelion	F
lustralis (Grt.)	"	"	"	dandelion, alfalfa	F
meditata (Grt.)	"	"	pinkbacked cutworm	dandelion	F
oliveacea (Morr.)	"	"	cutworm	"	F
renigera (Steph.)	"	"	bristly cutworm	dandelion, plantain	F
Lacon *brevicornis* LeC.	Coleoptera	Elateridae	click beetle	soil insect	F
obtectus Say	"	"	"	" "	F

SCIENTIFIC NAME	ORDER	FAMILY	COMMON NAME	MAIN HOST PLANT(S) OR INSECT TYPE	IMPORTANCE RATING
Lambdina fervidaria athasaria (Wlk.) f. *fiscellaria* (Gn.)	Lepidoptera "	Geometridae "	looper hemlock looper	deciduous general feeder	C A
Laothoe (= *Cressonia*) *juglandis* (J.E. Smith)	Lepidoptera	Sphingidae	walnut sphinx	walnut	C
Lapara bombycoides Wlk.	Lepidoptera	Sphingidae	pine tree sphinx	pine	C
Lasionma (= *Hylemya*) *anthracinum* (Czerny)	Diptera	Anthomyiidae	spruce cone maggot	spruce cones	A
(*Laspeyresia*) see *Cydia*					
(*Lecanium*) see *Parthenolecanium*					
Lepidosaphes ulmi (L.)	Homoptera	Coccidae	oystershell scale	fruit trees	B
Leptocoris trivittatus (Say)	Hemiptera	Rhopalidae	boxelder bug	Manitoba maple	C
Leptura subhamata Rand.	Coleoptera	Cerambycidae	longhorned beetle	red maple	C
Lepyrus alternans Casey *nordenskioldi canadensis* Casey	Coleoptera "	Curculionidae "	weevil poplar-willow leaf weevil	willow poplar, willow	C C
palustris Scop.	"	"	weevil	willow	C
Lestodiplosis grassator (Fyles)	Diptera	Cecidomyiidae	midge	probably a predator	D
Lethocerus americanus (Leidy)	Hemiptera	Belostomatidae	giant waterbug	aquatic	F

SCIENTIFIC NAME	ORDER	FAMILY	COMMON NAME	MAIN HOST PLANT(S) OR INSECT TYPE	IMPORTANCE RATING
(Leucania) see *Pseudaletia*					
Leucanthiza dircella Braun	Lepidoptera	Gracillariidae	leatherwood leafminer	leatherwood	C
Leucoma salicis (L.)	Lepidoptera	Lymantriidae	satin moth	poplar, willow	B
Leuconycta diphteroides (Gn.)	Lepidoptera	Noctuidae	marbled microcaelia	goldenrod	F
(Leucoptera) see *Paraleucoptera*					
(Limacodes) see *Apoda*					
(Limenitis) see *Basilarchia*					
Limonius aeger LeC.	Coleoptera	Elateridae	click beetle	soil insect	C
Lithacodes fasciola (H.-S.)	Lepidoptera	Limacodidae	slug caterpillar	deciduous	C
Lithacodia albidula (Gn.)	Lepidoptera	Noctuidae	owlet moth	grasses	C
(Lithocolletis) see *Phyllonorycter, Cameraria or Chrysaster*					
Litholomia napaea (Morr.)	Lepidoptera	Noctuidae	owlet moth	aspen	C
Lithomoia solidaginis (Hbn.)	Lepidoptera	Noctuidae	owlet moth	blueberry, labrador tea	C

SCIENTIFIC NAME	ORDER	FAMILY	COMMON NAME	MAIN HOST PLANT(S) OR INSECT TYPE	IMPORTANCE RATING
Lithophane					
amanda (Sm.)	Lepidoptera	Noctuidae	owlet moth	deciduous	C
antennata (Wlk.)	"	"	green fruitworm	apple	C
baileyi Grt.	"	"	owlet moth	choke cherry	C
bethunei (G. & R.)	"	"	"	deciduous	C
disposita Morr.	"	"	"	cherry, willow	C
fagina Morr.	"	"	"	birch	C
ferrealis Grt.	"	"	"	deciduous	C
georgii Grt.	"	"	"	"	C
grotei Riley	"	"	"	"	C
(= cinerosa Grt.)					
hemina Grt.	"	"	"	"	C
innominata (Sm.)	"	"	"	cherry	C
laticinerea Grt.	"	"	"	cherry, apple	C
lepida Grt.	"	"	"	pine	C
patefacta (Wlk.)	"	"	"	cherry	C
petulca Grt.	"	"	"	deciduous	C
pexata Grt.	"	"	"	general feeder	C
semiusta Grt.	"	"	"	deciduous	C
tepida Grt.	"	"	"	"	C
thaxteri Grt.	"	"	"	general feeder	C
unimoda (Lint.)	"	"	"	cherry	C
Lobophora					
nivigerata Wlk.	Lepidoptera	Geometridae	twolined aspen looper	aspen	C
Lochmaeus (see also *Heterocampa*)					
bilineata (Pack.)	Lepidoptera	Notodontidae	elm prominent	elm	C
manteo Dbly.	"	"	variable oakleaf caterpillar	deciduous	C
Lomanaltes					
eductalis (Wlk.)	Lepidoptera	Noctuidae	alder caterpillar	alder	C
Lomographa					
glomeraria (Grt.)	Lepidoptera	Geometridae	looper	deciduous	C
semiclarata (Wlk.)	"	"	wildcherry looper	"	C
vestaliata (Gn.)	"	"	looper	"	C

SCIENTIFIC NAME	ORDER	FAMILY	COMMON NAME	MAIN HOST PLANT(S) OR INSECT TYPE	IMPORTANCE RATING
Lophocampa see also *Halysidota*					
caryae Harr.	Lepidoptera	Arctiidae	hickory tussock moth	deciduous	C
maculata Harr.	"	"	spotted tussock moth	"	C
(Lophodonta) see *Peridea*					
Lucidota					
atra F.	Coleoptera	Lampyridae	firefly	predator	D
corrusca L.	"	"	"	"	D
nigricans Say	"	"	"	"	D
Lycaena					
phlaeas americana Harr.	Lepidoptera	Lycaenidae	American copper	*Rumex* spp.	C
Lycia					
ursaria (Wlk.)	Lepidoptera	Geometridae	stout spanworm	deciduous	C
Lycomorpha					
pholus (Drury)	Lepidoptera	Arctiidae	lichen caterpillar	lichen	F
Lygaeus					
kalmii Stål	Hemiptera	Lygaeidae	small milkweed bug	milkweed	F
(Lygris) see *Eulithis*					
Lymantor					
decipiens LeC.	Coleoptera	Scolytidae	bark beetle	deciduous	C
Lymantria					
dispar (L.)	Lepidoptera	Lymantriidae	gypsy moth	general feeder	A
Lytta					
sayi (LeC.)	Coleoptera	Meloidae	Say blister beetle	larva - predator, adult - general feeder	D
					C
Machimia					
tentoriferella Clem.	Lepidoptera	Oecophoridae	leaffolder	deciduous	C

SCIENTIFIC NAME	ORDER	FAMILY	COMMON NAME	MAIN HOST PLANT(S) OR INSECT TYPE	IMPORTANCE RATING
Macremphytus					
tarsatus (Say)	Hymenoptera	Tenthredinidae	dogwood sawfly	dogwood	C
(= *intermedius* (Dyar))					
testaceus (Nort.)	"	"	"	"	C
(= *varianus* (Nort.))					
Macrodactylus					
subspinosus (F.)	Coleoptera	Scarabaeidae	rose chafer	rose, wild grape	C
Macrohaltica (See also, *Altica*)					
ambiens (LeC.)	Coleoptera	Chrysomelidae	alder flea beetle	alder	B
populi (Brown)	"	"	poplar flea beetle	poplar	C
subplicata (LeC.)	"	"	willow flea beetle	willow	C
Macrophya					
punctumalbum (L.)	Hymenoptera	Tenthredinidae	European privet sawfly	privet	C
tibiator Nort.	"	"	sawfly	elderberry	C
Macroxyela					
ferruginea (Say)	Hymenoptera	Xyelidae	elm sawfly	elm	C
Macrurocampa					
marthesia (Cram.)	Lepidoptera	Notodontidae	hardwood caterpillar	oak, maple	C
Magdalis					
austera Fall	Coleoptera	Curculionidae	weevil	deciduous	C
austera substriga Fall	"	"		"	C
barbita (Say)	"	"	black elm bark weevil	"	C
perforata Horn	"	"	weevil	"	C
Malachius					
aeneus (L.)	Coleoptera	Melyridae	flower beetle	flowers	F
Malacosoma					
americanum (F.)	Lepidoptera	Lasiocampidae	eastern tent caterpillar	cherry	B
californicum lutescens (N. & D.)	"	"	prairie tent caterpillar	"	E
californicum pluviale (Dyar)	"	"	northern tent cater- pillar	"	B
disstria Hbn.	"	"	forest tent cater- pillar	aspen, deciduous	A

SCIENTIFIC NAME	ORDER	FAMILY	COMMON NAME	MAIN HOST PLANT(S) OR INSECT TYPE	IMPORTANCE RATING
Mamestra *curialis* (Sm.)	Lepidoptera	Noctuidae	garden armyworm	ground plants	F
Manduca *quinquemaculata* (Haw.)	Lepidoptera	Sphingidae	tomato hornworm	tomato, potato	G
sexta (L.)	"	"	tobacco hornworm	tobacco, tomato, potato	G
Mantis *religiosa* L.	Orthoptera	Mantidae	European mantid	predator	D
Marathyssa *inficita* Wlk.	Lepidoptera	Noctuidae	sumac caterpillar	sumac	C
Marmara *fasciella* (Cham.)	Lepidoptera	Gracillariidae	white pine bark miner	white pine	C
(Martyrhilda) see *Depressariodes*					
Matsucoccus *macrocicatrices* Rich.	Homoptera	Coccidae	white pine fungus scale	white pine	C
Mayetiola *carpophaga* (Tripp)	Diptera	Cecidomyiidae	spruce seed midge	spruce cone	C
celtiphyllia Felt	"	"	hackberry midge	hackberry	C
piceae (Felt)	"	"	spruce gall midge	spruce	C
rigidae (O. S.)	"	"	willow beaked gall midge	willow	C
ulmi (Beut.)	"	"	elm midge	elm	C
walshii Felt	"	"	clustered willow gall midge	willow	C
Meadorus *lateralis* Say	Hemiptera	Pentatomidae	mottled stink bug	predator	D
Mecas *inornata* Say	Coleoptera	Cerambycidae	poplar gall borer	poplar	C

SCIENTIFIC NAME	ORDER	FAMILY	COMMON NAME	MAIN HOST PLANT(S) OR INSECT TYPE	IMPORTANCE RATING
Mecyna *mustelinalis* (Pack.)	Lepidoptera	Pyralidae	micro moth	unknown	C
Megacyllene *caryae* (Gahan)	Coleoptera	Cerambycidae	painted hickory borer	hickory, ash	C
robiniae (Forst.)	"	"	locust borer	black locust	C
Meganola *minuscula* (Zell.)	Lepidoptera	Noctuidae (Nolinae)	oak caterpillar	white oak	C
Megarhyssa *macrurus macrurus* L.	Hymenoptera	Ichneumonidae	parasite	parasite	D
Megastigmus *atedius* Wlk. (= *piceae* Roh.)	Hymenoptera	Torymidae	spruce seed chalcid	spruce and white pine cones	C
laricis Marc.	"	"	larch "	larch	C
specularis Walley	"	"	balsam "	balsam fir	C
Megaxyela *major* (Cress.)	Hymenoptera	Xyelidae	hickory sawfly	hickory	C
(Melanagromyza) see *Napomyza*					
Melanchra (see also *Lacanobia, Papestra, Polia*) *adjuncta* (Gn.)	Lepidoptera	Noctuidae	hitched mamestra	deciduous	C
assimilis (Morr.)	"	"	cutworm	"	C
picta (Harr.)	"	"	zebra caterpillar	agricultural pest	F
pulverulenta (Sm.)	"	"	cutworm	general feeder	C
Melanolophia *canadaria* (Gn.)	Lepidoptera	Geometridae	variable redmarked looper	deciduous	C
imitata (Wlk.)	"	"	greenstriped forest looper	coniferous	C
signataria (Wlk.)	"	"	striped green looper	general feeder	C

SCIENTIFIC NAME	ORDER	FAMILY	COMMON NAME	MAIN HOST PLANT(S) OR INSECT TYPE	IMPORTANCE RATING
Melanophila					
acuminata DeG.	Coleoptera	Buprestidae	black fire beetle	coniferous	C
Melanotus					
castanipes Payk.	Coleoptera	Elateridae	click beetle	soil insects	F
leonardi LeC.	"	"	"	"	F
Melaphis					
rhois (Fitch)	Homoptera	Aphididae	sumac aphid	sumac	C
Melissopus					
latiferreanus (Wlsm.)	Lepidoptera	Olethreutinae	filbertworm	hazel	C
(Melitaea) see *Charidryas*					
Meloe					
americanus Leach	Coleoptera	Meloidae	buttercup oil beetle	larva – predator	D
				adult – general feeder	C
angusticollis Say	"	"	blister beetle	larva – predator	D
				adult – general feeder	C
Meoneura					
obscurella (Fall.)	Diptera	Milichiidae	European leafminer	deciduous	C
Meroptera					
abditiva Heinr.	Lepidoptera	Pyralidae	micro moth	poplar	C
pravella (Grt.)	"	"	lesser aspen webworm	aspen	C
Mesoleius					
tenthredinis Morley	Hymenoptera	Ichneumonidae	parasite	parasite	D
Messa					
nana (Klug)	Hymenoptera	Tenthredinidae	early birch leaf edgeminer	birch	C
populifoliella (Towns.)	"	"	poplar leafmining sawfly	poplar	C

SCIENTIFIC NAME	ORDER	FAMILY	COMMON NAME	MAIN HOST PLANT(S) OR INSECT TYPE	IMPORTANCE RATING
Metalepsis salicarum (Wlk.)	Lepidoptera	Noctuidae	owlet moth	unknown	C
Metallus rohweri MacG.	Hymenoptera	Tenthredinidae	blackberry leafminer	berry bushes	C
Metanema determinata Wlk.	Lepidoptera	Geometridae	looper	unknown	C
inatomaria Gn.	"	"	poplar looper	poplar	C
Microgoes oculatus (LeC.)	Coleoptera	Cerambycidae	longhorned wood borer	deciduous	C
Micurapteryx salicifoliella (Cham.)	Lepidoptera	Gracillariidae	willow leafminer	willow	B
Mindarus abietinus Koch	Homoptera	Aphididae	balsam twig aphid	balsam fir	C
Monochamus marmorator Kby.	Coleoptera	Cerambycidae	balsam fir sawyer	coniferous	B
mutator LeC.	"	"	sawyer beetle	"	C
notatus (Drury)	"	"	northeastern sawyer	"	B
scutellatus (Say)	"	"	whitespotted sawyer	"	A
Monoctenus fulvus (Nort.)	Hymenoptera	Diprionidae	cedar sawfly	cedar, juniper	C
suffusus (Cress.)	"	"	juniper sawfly	" "	C
(= *juniperinus* MacG.)	"	"	arborvitae sawfly	" "	C
Moodna ostrinella (Clem.)	Lepidoptera	Pyralidae	micro moth	sumac, oak	C
Mordwilkoja vagabunda (Walsh)	Homoptera	Aphididae	poplar vagabond aphid	poplar	C
Morrisonia (see also *Achatia*) *confusa* (Hbn.)	Lepidoptera	Noctuidae	owlet moth	deciduous	C

SCIENTIFIC NAME	ORDER	FAMILY	COMMON NAME	MAIN HOST PLANT(S) OR INSECT TYPE	IMPORTANCE RATING
Mulsantina hudsonica Casey *p. picta* (Rand.)	Coleoptera "	Coccinellidae "	lady beetle pine lady beetle	predator "	D D
Musca domestica L.	Diptera	Muscidae	house fly	household	G
Mycodiplosis cerasifolia Felt	Diptera	Cecidomyiidae	chokecherry leaf midge	chokecherry	C
Myzus cerasi (F.)	Homoptera	Aphididae	black cherry aphid	cherry	C
Nacophora quernaria (J.E. Smith)	Lepidoptera	Geometridae	oak beauty	deciduous	C
Nadata gibbosa (J.E. Smith)	Lepidoptera	Notodontidae	yellowlined cater-pillar	deciduous	C
Napomyza (= *Melanagromyza*) *schineri* (Gir.)	Diptera	Agromyzidae	poplar twig-gall fly	poplar	C
Neacanthocinus obsoletus Oliv. *pusillus* (Kby.)	Coleoptera "	Cerambycidae "	longhorned wood borer longhorned pine borer	coniferous pine	C C
Nealgedonia (see also *Phlyctaenia*) *extricalis* (Gn.)	Lepidoptera	Pyralidae	alder leaftier	alder	C
Nematocampa limbata (Haw.)	Lepidoptera	Geometridae	filament bearer	general feeder	C
Nematus (see also *Pontania*) *erythrogaster* Nort. *fulvicrus* Prov. *hudsoniimagnus* Dyar	Hymenoptera " "	Tenthredinidae " "	alder sawfly willow sawfly poplar sawfly	alder willow poplar	C C C

SCIENTIFIC NAME	ORDER	FAMILY	COMMON NAME	MAIN HOST PLANT(S) OR INSECT TYPE	IMPORTANCE RATING
Nematus (see also *Pontania*)					
latifasciatus Cress.	Hymenoptera	Tenthredinidae	willow sawfly	willow, birch	C
limbatus Cress.	"	"	"	willow, poplar	C
oligospilus Först.	"	"	willow-and-poplar sawfly	willow, poplar	C
(= *mendicus* Walsh)					
pinguidorsum Dyar	"	"	birch sawfly	birch	C
ribesii (Scop.)	"	"	imported currantworm	currant, gooseberry	C
salicisodoratus Dyar	"	"	willow sawfly	willow, poplar	C
umbratus Thoms.	"	"	alder sawfly	alder, birch	C
ventralis Say	"	"	willow sawfly	willow	C
Nemoria					
mimosaria (Gn.)	Lepidoptera	Geometridae	flanged looper	general feeder	C
rubrifrontaria (Pack.)	"	"	"	alder	C
Neoclytus					
acuminatus (F.)	Coleoptera	Cerambycidae	redheaded ash borer	ash	C
Neodiprion					
abbotii (Leach)	Hymenoptera	Diprionidae	pine sawfly	jack and red pine	C
abietis complex	"	"	balsam fir sawfly	balsam fir	A
compar (Leach)	"	"	pine sawfly	jack pine, red pine	C
lecontei (Fitch)	"	"	redheaded pine sawfly	pine	A
maurus Roh.	"	"	pine sawfly	jack pine	C
nanulus nanulus Schedl	"	"	red pine sawfly	red and jack pine	B
nigroscutum Midd.	"	"	pine sawfly	jack pine	C
pinetum (Nort.)	"	"	white pine sawfly	white pine	C
pratti banksianae Roh.	"	"	jack pine sawfly or blackheaded jack pine sawfly	jack pine	A
pratti paradoxicus Ross	"	"	jack pine sawfly	"	A
sertifer (Geoff.)	"	"	European pine sawfly	pine	A
swainei Midd.	"	"	Swaine jack pine sawfly	jack pine	A
virginiana complex	"	"	redheaded jack pine sawfly	"	A
Neomysia					
pullata randalli Casey	Coleoptera	Coccinellidae	lady beetle	predator	D
subvittata Muls.	"	"	"	"	D

SCIENTIFIC NAME	ORDER	FAMILY	COMMON NAME	MAIN HOST PLANT(S) OR INSECT TYPE	IMPORTANCE RATING
(Neosymydobius) see Symydobius					
Neotelphusa, (see also Pseudotelphusa and Telphusa) querciella (Cham.)	Lepidoptera	Gelechiidae	oak leafroller	white oak	C
Nephelodes minians Gn.(= emmedonius Cram.)	Lepidoptera	Noctuidae	bronzed cutworm	unknown	C
Nephopteryx basilaris Zell.	Lepidoptera	Pyralidae	micro moth	willow, poplar	C
carneella Hlst.	"	"	"	willow	C
subcaesiella (Clem.)	"	"	locust leafroller	locust	C
subfuscella (Rag.)	"	"	striped sumac leaf-roller	sumac	C
vetustella (Dyar)	"	"	basswood micro moth	basswood	C
virgatella (Clem.)	"	"	locust micro moth	locust	C
(Nepticula) see Stigmella, Ectoedemia					
Nepytia canosaria (Wlk.)	Lepidoptera	Geometridae	false hemlock looper	coniferous	C
Nerice bidentata Wlk.	Lepidoptera	Notodontidae	prominent moth	elm	C
Neuroterus exiguissimus Bass.	Hymenoptera	Cynipidae	oak gall wasp	oak	C
quercusbatatus (Fitch)	"	"	oak potato gall wasp	white oak	C
saltarius Weld.	"	"	oak gall wasp	oak	C
umbilicatus Bass.	"	"	"	"	C
vernus Gill.	"	"	"	"	C
Neurotoma fasciata (Nort.)	Hymenoptera	Pamphiliidae	cherry webspinning sawfly	cherry	C
inconspicua (Nort.)	"	"	plum webspinning sawfly	"	C

SCIENTIFIC NAME	ORDER	FAMILY	COMMON NAME	MAIN HOST PLANT(S) OR INSECT TYPE	IMPORTANCE RATING
Nites					
betulella (Bsk.)	Lepidoptera	Oecophoridae	blackdotted birch leaftier	birch	C
groteella (Rob.)	"	"	hazel leaftier	hazel	C
ostryella (McD.)	"	"	ironwood leaftier	ironwood	C
Nomius					
pygmaeus (Dej.)	Coleoptera	Carabidae	stink beetle	predator	D
Notodonta (see also Peridea)					
simplaria Graef	Lepidoptera	Notodontidae	humped caterpillar	poplar, willow	C
scitipennis Wlk.	"	"	"	"	C
Nycteola					
cinereana N. & D.	Lepidoptera	Noctuidae	poplar leaftier	poplar	C
frigidana (Wlk.)	"	"	willow leaftier	willow	C
(Nyctobia) see *Cladara*					
(Nygmia) see *Euproctis*					
Nymphalis (see also Aglais)					
antiopa (L.)	Lepidoptera	Nymphalidae	mourningcloak butter-fly, spiny elm caterpillar	deciduous	C
vau-album j-album (Bdv. & LeC.)	"	"	Compton tortoiseshell	"	C
Oberea					
schaumii LeC.	Coleoptera	Cerambycidae	poplar branch borer	poplar	C
tripunctata (Swed.)	"	"	dogwood twig borer	dogwood	C
Obolodiplosis					
robiniae (Hald.)	Diptera	Cecidomyiidae	locust gall midge	locust	C
Obrussa					
ochrefasciella (Cham.)	Lepidoptera	Nepticulidae	hard maple budminer	sugar maple	C
sericopeza (Zell.)	"	"	Norway maple seedminer	Norway maple	C

SCIENTIFIC NAME	ORDER	FAMILY	COMMON NAME	MAIN HOST PLANT(S) OR INSECT TYPE	IMPORTANCE RATING
Ochropleura plecta (L.)	Lepidoptera	Noctuidae	flameshouldered dart	clover	C
Ocnerostoma strobivorum Free.	Lepidoptera	Yponomeutidae	white pine needle-miner	white pine	C
Odontopus calceatus Say	Coleoptera	Curculionidae	tuliptree leafminer	tulip tree	C
Odontosia elegans (Stkr.)	Lepidoptera	Notodontidae	aspen caterpillar	aspen	C
Odontota dorsalis (Thunb.)	Coleoptera	Chrysomelidae	locust leafminer	locust, deciduous	B
Oidaematophorus species	Lepidoptera	Pterophoridae	plume moths	ground plants	C
Okanagana canadensis (Prov.)	Homoptera	Cicadidae	cicada	larva in soil	C
rimosa (Say)	"	"	"	" " "	C
Olethreutes (= *Exartema*)	Lepidoptera	Olethreutinae			
appendicea (Zell.)			leafroller	deciduous	C
atrodentana (Fern.)	"	"	oak leafroller	oak	C
bipartitana (Clem.)	"	"	micro moth	hazel	C
cespitana (Hbn.)	"	"	"	aspen	C
clavana (Wlk.)	"	"	leafroller	elm	C
connectus (McD.)	"	"	dogwood leaf roller	dogwood	C
corylana (Fern.)	"	"	leafroller	hazel	C
costimaculana (Fern.)	"	"	labrador tea micro moth	labrador tea	C
fasciatana (Clem.)	"	"	leafroller	poplar, willow	C
glaciana (Mösch.)	"	"	micro moth	deciduous	C
inornatana (Clem.)	"	"	cherry leafroller	cherry	C
merrickana (Kft.)	"	"	ironwood leafroller	ironwood, hickory	C
nigrana (Heinr.)	"	"	basswood leafroller	basswood, maple	C
permundana (Clem.)	"	"	raspberry leafroller	raspberry	C
punctana (Wlsm.)	"	"	dogwood leafroller	dogwood	C
quadrifidus (Zell.)	"	"	leafroller	chokecherry	C
tiliana (Heinr.)	"	"	basswood leafroller	basswood	C
zelleriana (Fern.)	"	"	viburnum leafroller	wire birch	C

SCIENTIFIC NAME	ORDER	FAMILY	COMMON NAME	MAIN HOST PLANT(S) OR INSECT TYPE	IMPORTANCE RATING
Oligia illocata (Wlk.)	Lepidoptera	Noctuidae	owlet moth	deciduous	C
Oligocentria ligmicolor (Wlk.)	Lepidoptera	Notodontidae	lacecapped caterpillar	deciduous	C
Oligonychus milleri (McG.)	Acari	Tetranychidae	pine spider mite	pine	C
ununguis (Jac.)	"	"	spruce spider mite	spruce	B
Oligotrophus species	Diptera	Cecidomyiidae	gall or tip midges	juniper and others	C
Oneida lunulalis (Hlst.)	Lepidoptera	Pyralidae	micro moth	oak	C
Operophtera bruceata (Hlst.)	Lepidoptera	Geometridae	Bruce spanworm	sugar maple, aspen	B
brumata (L.)	"	"	winter moth	deciduous	E
Ophioderma pubescens (Emm.)	Homoptera	Membracidae	treehopper	deciduous	C
Oreana unicolorella (Hlst.)	Lepidoptera	Pyralidae	micro moth	deciduous	C
Orgilus obscurator (Nees)	Hymenoptera	Braconidae	parasite	parasite of European pine shoot moth	D
Orgyia antiqua (L.)	Lepidoptera	Lymantriidae	rusty tussock moth	general feeder	C
leucostigma intermedia Fitch	"	"	white-marked tussock moth	"	C
Ormenis pruinosa Say	Homoptera	Flatidae	planthopper	elm	C
Orsodacne atra Ahr.	Coleoptera	Chrysomelidae	leaf beetle	willow catkins	C

SCIENTIFIC NAME	ORDER	FAMILY	COMMON NAME	MAIN HOST PLANT(S) OR INSECT TYPE	IMPORTANCE RATING
Orthodes cynica Gn.	Lepidoptera	Noctuidae	cutworm	unknown	C
Ortholepis pasadamia (Dyar)	Lepidoptera	Pyralidae	striped birch pyralid	birch	C
Orthosia hibisci (Gn.)	Lepidoptera	Noctuidae	speckled green fruit-worm	deciduous	C
revicta (Morr.)	"	"	rusty whitesided caterpillar	"	C
rubescens (Wlk.)	"	"	owlet moth	"	C
Orthosoma brunneum (Först.)	Coleoptera	Cerambycidae	brown prionid	dead wood	C
Orthotaenia undulana (D. & S.)	Lepidoptera	Olethreutinae	leafroller	deciduous	C
Orthotomicus caelatus (Eichh.)	Coleoptera	Scolytidae	bark beetle	coniferous	C
Osmoderma eremicola Knoch	Coleoptera	Scarabaeidae	scarab beetle	fruit trees	C
scabra Beauv.	"	"	"	"	C
Otiorhynchus ovatus (L.)	Coleoptera	Curculionidae	strawberry rootweevil	coniferous roots	A
sulcatus (F.)	"	"	black vine weevil	general feeder	C
Pachypappa tremulae (L.)	Homoptera	Aphididae	aspen aphid	aspen	C
Pachypsylla celtidismamma (Riley)	Homoptera	Psyllidae	hackberry nipplegall maker	hackberry	C
globulus Riley	"	"	hackberry leaf gall	"	C
Pachysphinx modesta (Harr.)	Lepidoptera	Sphingidae	big poplar sphinx	deciduous	C

SCIENTIFIC NAME	ORDER	FAMILY	COMMON NAME	MAIN HOST PLANT(S) OR INSECT TYPE	IMPORTANCE RATING
Packardia ceanothi Dyar *elegans* (Pack.)	Lepidoptera "	Limacodidae "	slug caterpillar "	white birch chestnut, beech	C C
Paleacrita vernata (Peck)	Lepidoptera	Geometridae	spring cankerworm	elm, sugar maple	C
Palpita magniferalis (Wlk.)	Lepidoptera	Pyralidae	ash leafroller	ash	C
Palthis angulalis (Hbn.)	Lepidoptera	Noctuidae	spruce harlequin	spruce	C
Pamphilius ochreipes (Cress.)	Hymenoptera	Pamphiliidae	viburnum webspinning sawfly	cranberry	C
Pandemis canadana Kft. *lamprosana* (Rob.) *limitata* (Rob.)	Lepidoptera " "	Tortricidae " "	green aspen leaftier leafroller threelined leafroller	deciduous " "	C C C
Panopoda carneicosta Gn. *rufimargo* (Hbn.)	Lepidoptera "	Noctuidae "	owlet moth " "	deciduous oak, beech	C C
Panthea acronyctoides (Wlk.) *furcilla* (Pack.) *pallescens centralis* McD.	Lepidoptera " "	Noctuidae " "	tufted spruce caterpillar tufted white pine caterpillar tufted pine caterpillar	coniferous " "	C C C
Pantographa limata (G. & R.)	Lepidoptera	Pyralidae	basswood leafroller	basswood, elm	C

SCIENTIFIC NAME	ORDER	FAMILY	COMMON NAME	MAIN HOST PLANT(S) OR INSECT TYPE	IMPORTANCE RATING
Paonias					
excaecatus (J.E. Smith)	Lepidoptera	Sphingidae	blindeyed sphinx	deciduous	C
myops (J.E. Smith)	"	"	smalleyed sphinx	serviceberry	C
Papaipema					
cataphracta (Grt.)	Lepidoptera	Noctuidae	burdock borer	burdock	F
unimodia (Sm.)	"	"	borer	meadow-rue, cone-flower	C
Papestra (see also *Lacanobia, Melanchra, Polia*)					
cristifera (Wlk.)	Lepidoptera	Noctuidae	cutworm	general feeder	C
quadrata ingravis (Sm.)	"	"	"	deciduous	C
Papilio					
cresphontes Cram.	Lepidoptera	Papilionidae	orangedog	deciduous	C
glaucus L.	"	"	tiger swallowtail	"	C
glaucus canadensis R. & J.	"	"	Canadian tiger swallowtail	"	C
philenor (L.) (see *Battus*)					
polyxenes asterius Stoll	"	"	black swallowtail, or celeryworm, or parsleyworm	parsley, etc.	G
troilus L.	"	"	spicebush swallowtail	shrubs	C
Paraclemensia					
acerifoliella (Fitch)	Lepidoptera	Incurvariidae	maple leafcutter	maple	B
Paradiplosis					
tumifex Gagné	Diptera	Cecidomyiidae	balsam gall midge	balsam fir	B
Paraleucoptera					
albella (Cham.)	Lepidoptera	Lyonetiidae	cottonwood leafminer	poplar	C
Parallelia					
bistriaris Hbn.	Lepidoptera	Noctuidae	maple caterpillar	maple, birch	C
(*Paralobesia*) see *Endopiza*					

SCIENTIFIC NAME	ORDER	FAMILY	COMMON NAME	MAIN HOST PLANT(S) OR INSECT TYPE	IMPORTANCE RATING
Paraphytomyza populicola (Wlk.)	Diptera	Agromyzidae	Lombardy leafminer	poplar	C
(*Paraprociphilus*) see *Prociphilus*					
(*Parasemia*) see *Platarctia*					
Parastichtis discivaria (Wlk.)	Lepidoptera	Noctuidae	owlet moth	poplar	C
Parcoblatta pennsylvanica (DeG.)	Orthoptera	Blattidae	Pennsylvania wood cockroach	vegetable matter	F
Parectopa robiniella Clem.	Lepidoptera	Gracillariidae	locust digitate leafminer	locust	C
(*Pareophora*) see *Eupareophora*					
(*Parorgyia*) see *Dasychira*					
Parornix conspicuella (Dietz)	Lepidoptera	Gracillariidae	birch micro moth	birch	C
Parthenolecanium (= *Lecanium*) *corni* (Bouché)	Homoptera	Coccidae	European fruit lecanium or brown elm scale	fruit tres	B
fletcheri (Ckll.)	"	"	Fletcher scale	cedar, juniper, yew	B
quercifex (Fitch)	"	"	oak lecanium	oak	C
Patelloa pachypyga (A. & W.)	Diptera	Tachinidae	parasite	parasite	D
Pemphigus populicaulis Fitch	Homoptera	Aphididae	poplar leaf petiole-gall aphid	poplar	C

SCIENTIFIC NAME	ORDER	FAMILY	COMMON NAME	MAIN HOST PLANT(S) OR INSECT TYPE	IMPORTANCE RATING
Pemphigus					
populi-globuli Fitch	Homoptera	Aphididae	poplar bulletgall aphid	balsam poplar	C
populitransversus Riley	"	"	poplar petiolegall aphid	poplar	C
Pennisetia					
marginata (Harr.)	Lepidoptera	Sesiidae	raspberry crown borer	raspberry	C
Pentamerismus					
canadensis MacG.	Acari	Tenuipalpidae	false spider mite	cedar	C
erythreus (Ewing)	"	"	"	cedar, juniper	C
Periclista					
albicollis (Nort.)	Hymenoptera	Tenthredinidae	oak sawfly	oak	C
diluta (Cress.)	"	"	"	"	C
media (Nort.)	"	"	"	"	C
Peridea (see also *Notodonta*)					
angulosa (J.E. Smith)	Lepidoptera	Notodontidae	oak caterpillar	oak	C
basitriens (Wlk.)	"	"	rednarked caterpillar	elm	C
ferruginea (Pack.)	"	"	birch caterpillar	birch	C
Peridroma					
saucia (Hbn.)	Lepidoptera	Noctuidae	variegated cutworm	nursery, field and garden plants	C
Perilampus					
hyalinus Say	Hymenoptera	Perilampidae	parasite	parasite	D
Periphyllus					
lyropictus (Kess.)	Homoptera	Aphididae	Norway maple aphid	Norway maple	B
negundinis (Thos.)	"	"	boxelder aphid	Manitoba maple	C
Pero					
honestaria (Wlk.)	Lepidoptera	Geometridae	looper	general feeder	C
hubneraria (Gn.)	"	"	"	deciduous	C
morrisonaria (Hy. Edw.)	"	"	"	general feeder	C

SCIENTIFIC NAME	ORDER	FAMILY	COMMON NAME	MAIN HOST PLANT(S) OR INSECT TYPE	IMPORTANCE RATING
Petrophora *subaequaria* (Wlk.)	Lepidoptera	Geometridae	leaping looper	chokecherry	C
Petrova *albicapitana* (Bsk.)	Lepidoptera	Olethreutinae	northern pitch twig moth	jack pine	C
comstockiana (Fern.)	"	"	pitch twig moth	pitch pine	C
gemistrigulana (Kft.)	"	"	pine bark moth	pine	C
wenzeli (Kft.)	"	"	pitch nodule moth	"	C
(*Phalonia*) see *Aethes, Hysterosia*					
(*Phenacaspis*) see *Chionaspis*					
Pheosia *rimosa* Pack.	Lepidoptera	Notodontidae	false hornworm	poplar, willow	C
Phigalia *strigataria* (Minot)	Lepidoptera	Geometridae	looper	elm	C
titea (Cram.)	"	"	spiny looper	deciduous	C
(*Phlegethontius*) see *Manduca*					
Phloeosinus *canadensis* Swaine	Coleoptera	Scolytidae	nothern cedar bark beetle	cedar	C
Phloeotribus *liminarus* (Harr.)	Coleoptera	Scolytidae	peach bark beetle	cherry	C
picea Swaine	"	"	spruce bark beetle	spruce	C
Phlogophora *iris* Gn.	Lepidoptera	Noctuidae	cutworm	unknown	C
periculosa Gn.	"	"	"	general feeder	C
Phlyctaenia (see also *Nealgedonia*) *coronata tertialis* (Gn.)	Lepidoptera	Pyralidae	elderberry leaftier	elderberry	C

SCIENTIFIC NAME	ORDER	FAMILY	COMMON NAME	MAIN HOST PLANT(S) OR INSECT TYPE	IMPORTANCE RATING
Phobetron pithecium (J.E. Smith)	Lepidoptera	Limacodidae	hagmoth	sugar maple	C
Pholisora catullus (F.)	Lepidoptera	Hesperiidae	common sooty wing	ground plants	F
(Pholus) see *Eumorpha*					
Phragmatobia assimilans Wlk.	Lepidoptera	Arctiidae	dusky red tiger moth	deciduous	C
Phratora americana canadensis Brown	Coleoptera	Chrysomelidae	American willow leaf beetle	willow	C
frosti remissa Brown	"	"	leaf beetle	"	C
hudsonia Brown	"	"	birch leaf beetle	birch	C
p. purpurea Brown	"	"	aspen skeletonizer	poplar	C
Phyllobius oblongus (L.)	Coleoptera	Curculionidae	European snout beetle	deciduous	C
Phyllocnistis populiella (Cham.)	Lepidoptera	Gracillariidae	aspen serpentine leafminer	poplar	C
vitifoliella Cham.	"	"	grape serpentine leafminer	grapevine	C
Phyllocolpa agama (Roh.)	Hymenoptera	Tenthredinidae	willow leaffolding sawfly	willow	C
bozemani (Cooley)	"	"	poplar leaffolding sawfly	poplar	C
mariana (Ross)	"	"	poplar leaffolding sawfly	"	C
popuella (Ross)	"	"	poplar edgefolding sawfly	"	C
populi (Marl.)	"	"	poplar leafgall sawfly	"	C
Phyllocoptes didelphis Keif.	Acari	Eriophyidae	poplar felt mite	poplar	C

SCIENTIFIC NAME	ORDER	FAMILY	COMMON NAME	MAIN HOST PLANT(S) OR INSECT TYPE	IMPORTANCE RATING
Phyllodesma					
americana (Harr.)	Lepidoptera	Lasciocampidae	lappet moth	deciduous	C
Phyllonorycter	Lepidoptera	Gracillariidae			
alnicolella (Wlsm.)	"	"	alder leafblotch miner	alder	C
argentifimbriella (Clem.)	"	"	oak leafblotch miner	oak	C
basistrigella (Clem.)	"	"	oak leafblotch miner	"	C
celtisella (Cham.)	"	"	hackberry leafblotch miner	hackberry	C
kenora (Free.)	"	"	willow leafblotch miner	willow	C
lucetiella (Clem.)	"	"	basswood squareblotch miner	basswood	C
lucidicostella (Clem.)	"	"	lesser maple leafblotch miner	maple	C
malimalifoliella (Braun)	"	"	apple leafblotch miner	apple	C
nipigon (Free.)	"	"	balsam poplar leafblotch miner	balsam, poplar	B
ontario (Free.)	"	"	aspen leafblotch miner	aspen	B
ostraefoliella (Clem.)	"	"	ironwood leafblotch miner	ironwood	C
propinquinella (Braun)	"	"	cherry leafblotch miner	cherry	C
robiniella (Clem.)	"	"	locust leafblotch miner	locust	C
salicifoliella (Cham.) see also spp. *kenora, nipigon,* and *ontario*	"	"	willow leafblotch miner	willow	C
tilliacella (Cham.)	"	"	basswood roundblotch miner	basswood	C
Phyllophaga	Coleoptera	Scarabaeidae			
anxia LeC.	"	"	common June beetle	soil insect	B
drakei (Kby.)	"	"	June beetle	"	B
fusca (Frö.)	"	"	northern June beetle	"	B
futilis LeC.	"	"	lesser June beetle	"	B
rugosa (Melsh.)	"	"	rugose June beetle	"	B
(*Phylloxera*) see *Xerophylla*					
Physokermes	Homoptera	Coccidae			
piceae (Schr.)			spruce bud scale	spruce	C

SCIENTIFIC NAME	ORDER	FAMILY	COMMON NAME	MAIN HOST PLANT(S) OR INSECT TYPE	IMPORTANCE RATING
(Phytagromyza) see *Paraphytomyza*					
Phytobia					
amelanchieris (Greene)	Diptera	Agromyzidae	amelanchier twig borer	amelanchier	C
betulivora Spencer	"	"	birch cambium miner	birch	C
pleuralis (Mall.)	"	"	catalpa leafminer	catalpa	C
setosa (Loew)	"	"	red maple cambium borer	red maple	C
Phytocoptella					
abnormis (Gar.)	Acari	Eriophyidae	linden gall mite	basswood	C
(Pieris) see *Artogeia*					
Pikonema					
alaskensis (Roh.)	Hymenoptera	Tenthredinidae	yellowheaded spruce sawfly	spruce	A
dimmockii (Cress.)	"	"	greenheaded spruce sawfly	"	C
Pineus					
floccus (Patch)	Homoptera	Phylloxeridae (= Adelgidae)	redspruce adelgid	spruce	C
pinifoliae (Fitch)	"	"	pine leaf adelgid	spruce, pine	C
similis (Gill.)	"	"	ragged sprucegall adelgid	spruce	C
strobi (Htg.)	"	"	pine bark adelgid	pine	B
Pissodes					
affinis Rand.	Coleoptera	Curculionidae	bark weevil	pine, spruce	C
approximatus Hopk.	"	"	northern pine weevil	pine	B
dubius Rand.	"	"	balsam bark weevil	balsam fir, spruce	C
rotundatus LeC.	"	"	small spruce weevil	spruce, pine	C
similis Hopk.	"	"	balsam fir weevil	balsam fir	C
strobi (Peck)	"	"	white pine weevil	pine, spruce	A
Pityogenes					
hopkinsi Swaine	Coleoptera	Scolytidae	bark beetle	pine	C
plagiatus LeC.	"	"	" "	pine, spruce	C

SCIENTIFIC NAME	ORDER	FAMILY	COMMON NAME	MAIN HOST PLANT(S) OR INSECT TYPE	IMPORTANCE RATING
Pityokteines sparsus (LeC.)	Coleoptera	Scolytidae	balsam fir bark beetle	balsam fir	C
Pityophthorus cariniceps LeC. (= *canadensis* Swaine)	Coleoptera	Scolytidae	bark beetle	coniferous	C
consimilis LeC.	"	"	"	"	C
lautus Eich.	"	"	"	"	C
puberulus LeC.	"	"	pith borer	"	C
pulchellus Eich.	"	"	pine bark borer	pine	C
pulicarius (Zimm.)	"	"	pine pith borer	"	C
rhois Swaine	"	"	sumac bark beetle	sumac	C
Plagiodera versicolora (Laich.)	Coleoptera	Chrysomelidae	imported willow leaf beetle	willow	B
Plagiometriona clavata F.	Coleoptera	Chrysomelidae	leaf beetle	basswood	C
Plagodis alcoolaria (Gn.)	Lepidoptera	Geometridae	birch looper	deciduous	C
kuetzingi (Grt.)	"	"	looper	"	C
phlogosaria (Gn.)	"	"	"	"	C
serinaria H.-S.	"	"	"	"	C
Platarctia parthenos (Harr.)	Lepidoptera	Arctiidae	giant tiger moth	deciduous	C
Plathypena scabra F.	Lepidoptera	Noctuidae	green cloverworm	clover	G
Platycerus marginalis Casey	Coleoptera	Lucanidae	stag beetle	coniferous	C
Platynota idaeusalis (Wlk.)	Lepidoptera	Tortricidae	leafroller	goldenrod, deciduous	C
Platyperigea multifera (Wlk.)	Lepidoptera	Noctuidae	rustic	unknown	C

SCIENTIFIC NAME	ORDER	FAMILY	COMMON NAME	MAIN HOST PLANT(S) OR INSECT TYPE	IMPORTANCE RATING
Platyptilia (= *Amblyptilia* in part) *pallidactyla* (Haw.) (*punctidactyla* Haw.)	Lepidoptera	Pterophoridae	plume moth	unknown	C
Platypolia anceps (Steph.)	Lepidoptera	Noctuidae	owlet moth	unknown	C
Plemyria georgii Hlst.	Lepidoptera	Geometridae	looper	deciduous	C
Pleroneura brunneicornis Roh. (= *borealis* Felt)	Hymenoptera	Xyelidae	balsam shootboring sawfly	balsam fir	C
Plodia interpunctella (Hbn.)	Lepidoptera	Pyralidae	Indian meal moth	household	G
Plusia putnami Grt.	Lepidoptera	Noctuidae	owlet moth	grass	C
Plutella xylostella (L.) (= *maculipennis* Curt.)	Lepidoptera	Plutellidae	diamond back moth	cabbage, etc.	G
Poanes hobomok (Harr.)	Lepidoptera	Hesperiidae	hobomok skipper	unknown	C
Podabrus diadema F.	Coleoptera	Cantharidae	soldier beetle	predator	D
modestus Say	"	"	"	"	D
tomentosus Say	"	"	"	"	D
Podapion gallicola Riley	Coleoptera	Curculionidae	pine gall weevil	red pine	C
Podisus maculiventris (Say)	Hemiptera	Pentatomidae	spined soldier bug	predator	D
modestus Dall.	"	"	stink bug	"	D
placidus Uhl.	"	"	"	"	D
serieventris Uhl.	"	"	"	"	D

SCIENTIFIC NAME	ORDER	FAMILY	COMMON NAME	MAIN HOST PLANT(S) OR INSECT TYPE	IMPORTANCE RATING
Podosesia *syringae* (Harr.) (= *fraxina* Lug.)	Lepidoptera	Sesiidae	ash borer, lilac borer	ash, lilac	C
Polia (see also *Lacanobia,* *Melanchra, Papestra*)	Lepidoptera	Noctuidae	cutworm	deciduous	C
detracta (Wlk.)	"	"	"	cherry	C
imbrifera (Gn.)	"	"	"	birch	C
latex (Gn.)	"	"	"	deciduous	C
nimbosa (Gn.)	"	"	"	unknown	C
obscura (Sm.)	"	"	"	willow	C
purpurissata (Grt.)					
Polites *mystic* (Edw.)	Lepidoptera	Hesperiidae	long dash	grasses	F
Polydrusus *impressifrons* Gyll.	Coleoptera	Curculionidae	pale green weevil	deciduous	C
Polygonia *comma* Harr.	Lepidoptera	Nymphalidae	hop merchant	deciduous	C
faunus (Edw.)	"	"	green comma	"	C
interrogationis (F.)	"	"	question mark	"	C
progne (Cram.)	"	"	gray comma	"	C
Polygraphus *rufipennis* (Kby.)	Coleoptera	Scolytidae	foureyed spruce bark beetle	spruce	C
Pontania (see also *Nematus*) *lucidae* Roh.	Hymenoptera	Tenthredinidae	willow gall sawfly	willow	C
proxima (Lep.)	"	"	willow redgall sawfly	"	C
resinicola Marl.	"	"	willow leafgall sawfly	"	C
s-pomum (Walsh) (= *hospes* Walsh)	"	"	willow apple gall sawfly	"	C
Popillia *japonica* Newm.	Coleoptera	Scarabaeidae	Japanese beetle	general feeder	C
(*Porthetria*) see *Lymantria*					

SCIENTIFIC NAME	ORDER	FAMILY	COMMON NAME	MAIN HOST PLANT(S) OR INSECT TYPE	IMPORTANCE RATING
Prionoxystus					
macmurtrei (Guer.)	Lepidoptera	Cossidae	little carpenterworm	deciduous	C
robiniae (Peck)	"	"	carpenterworm	"	C
Priophorus					
betulae Roh.	Hymenoptera	Tenthredinidae	birch sawfly	birch	C
infuscatus (MacG.)	"	"	willow sawfly	willow	C
Pristiphora					
acidovalva Wong	Hymenoptera	Tenthredinidae	willow sawfly	willow	C
cadma W. & R.	"	"	birch sawfly	birch	C
erichsonii (Htg.)	"	"	larch sawfly	larch	A
geniculata (Htg.)	"	"	mountain ash sawfly	mountain-ash	A
lena Kinc.	"	"	little spruce sawfly	spruce	C
micronematica Malaise	"	"	willow sawfly	willow	C
Probole (= *Hyperetis*)					
amicaria (H.-S.)	Lepidoptera	Geometridae	redcheeked looper	alder	C
alienaria H.-S.	"	"	looper	maple	C
Prochoerodes					
transversata (Drury)	Lepidoptera	Geometridae	large maple looper	deciduous	C
Prociphilus (= *Paraprociphilus*)					
tessellatus (Fitch)	Homoptera	Aphididae	woolly alder aphid	alder, maple	B
Prodiplosis					
morrisi Gagné	Diptera	Cecidomyiidae	leafcurl midge	poplar	B
Profenusa					
canadensis (Marl.)	Hymenoptera	Tenthredinidae	hawthorn leafmining sawfly	hawthorn	C
lucifex (Ross)	"	"	oak leafmining sawfly	oak	B
thomsoni (Konow)	"	"	ambermarked birch leafminer	birch	B
Proleucoptera					
(*albella* Cham.)					
see *Paraleucoptera*					
smilaciella Bsk.	Lepidoptera	Lyonetiidae	greenbrier leafminer	greenbrier	C

SCIENTIFIC NAME	ORDER	FAMILY	COMMON NAME	MAIN HOST PLANT(S) OR INSECT TYPE	IMPORTANCE RATING
Prolimacodes badia (Hbn.)	Lepidoptera	Limacodidae	slug caterpillar	deciduous	C
Proserpinus flavofasciata (Wlk.)	Lepidoptera	Sphingidae	yellowbanded day sphinx	ground plants	C
Prosimulium mixtum S. and D.	Diptera	Simuliidae	black fly	biting insect	F
Protagrotis niveivenosa (Grt.)	Lepidoptera	Noctuidae	owlet moth	unknown	C
Proteoteras aesculana Riley	Lepidoptera	Olethreutinae	maple twig borer	maple	C
moffatiana Fern.	"	"	maple shoot borer	"	C
willingana (Kft.)	"	"	boxelder twig borer	Manitoba maple	C
Protheca puberula LeC.	Coleoptera	Anobiidae	deathwatch beetle	dry wood	F
Protitame virginalis (Hlst.)	Lepidoptera	Geometridae	poplar looper	deciduous	C
Protoboarmia porcelaria indicataria (Wlk.)	Lepidoptera	Geometridae	dashlined looper	coniferous	C
(Protolachnus) see Eulachnus					
Protolampra rufipectus (Morr.)	Lepidoptera	Noctuidae	owlet moth	deciduous	C
Protorthodes oviduca (Gn.)	Lepidoptera	Noctuidae	owlet moth	ground plants	F
Proxenus miranda (Grt.)	Lepidoptera	Noctuidae	dandelion cutworm	dandelion	F
Pseudaletia unipuncta (Haw.)	Lepidoptera	Noctuidae	armyworm	general feeder	C

SCIENTIFIC NAME	ORDER	FAMILY	COMMON NAME	MAIN HOST PLANT(S) OR INSECT TYPE	IMPORTANCE RATING
Pseudexentera					
costomaculana Clem.	Lepidoptera	Olethreutinae	witch hazel leafroller	witch hazel	C
cressoniana Clem.	"	"	hickory leafroller	hickory	C
mali Free.	"	"	pale apple leafroller	apple	C
oregonana (Wlsm.)	"	"	early aspen leafcurler	poplar	A
Spoliana Clem.	"	"	oak olethreutid leafroller	oak	C
Pseudochelaria					
walsinghami Dietz	Lepidoptera	Gelechiidae	sumac micro moth	sumac	C
Pseudolucanus					
placidus (Say)	Coleoptera	Lucanidae	stag beetle	decayed wood	F
Pseudosciaphila					
duplex (Wlsm.)	Lepidoptera	Olethreutinae	spotted aspen leafroller	poplar	B
Pseudorthodes					
vecors (Gn.)	Lepidoptera	Noctuidae	cutworm	ground plants	F
Pseudotelphusa, (see also *Telphusa* and *Neotelphusa*)					
belangerella (Cham.)	Lepidoptera	Gelechiidae	alder leafroller	alder	C
Pseudothyatira					
cymatophoroides Gn.	Lepidoptera	Thyatiridae	birch-and-alder caterpillar	birch, alder	C
Psilocorsis					
cryptolechiella (Cham) (= faginella [Cham.])	Lepidoptera	Oecophoridae	twoleaf tier	oak, others	C
quercicella Clem.	"	"	oak leaftier	"	C
reflexella Clem. (= fletcherella Gibs.)	"	"	flat leaftier	"	C
Psyche					
casta (Pallas)	Lepidoptera	Psychidae	bagworm	deciduous	C

SCIENTIFIC NAME	ORDER	FAMILY	COMMON NAME	MAIN HOST PLANT(S) OR INSECT TYPE	IMPORTANCE RATING
Psylla					
floccosa (Patch)	Homoptera	Psyllidae	false woolly alder aphid	alder	C
negundinis Mally	"	"	boxelder psyllid	Manitoba maple	C
striata Patch	"	"	birch psyllid	birch	C
Psyllobora					
viginti-maculata (Say)	Coleoptera	Coccinellidae	lady beetle	predator	D
Pterocomma					
populifoliae (Fitch)	Homoptera	Aphididae	poplar aphid	poplar	C
smithiae (Monell)	"	"	black willow aphid	poplar, willow	C
Pteronarcys					
dorsata Say	Plecoptera	Pteronarcidae	stone fly	aquatic insect	F
Pterostichus					
mutus Say	Coleoptera	Carabidae	ground beetle	predator	D
Ptilinus					
ruficornis Say	Coleoptera	Anobiidae	deathwatch beetle	dry wood	F
(Pulicalvaria) see *Coleotechnites*					
Pulvinaria					
innumerabilis (Rathv.)	Homoptera	Coccidae	cottony maple scale	maple	C
Pyractomena					
borealis Rand.	Coleoptera	Lampyridae	firefly	predator	D
Pyrrhalta					
alni (Fall.)	Coleoptera	Chrysomelidae	brown alder leaf beetle	alder	C
cavicollis (LeC.)	"	"	cherry leaf beetle	cherry	C
decora decora (Say)	"	"	gray willow leaf beetle	willow	B
luteola (Müll.)	"	"	elm leaf beetle	elm	C
nymphaeae (L.)	"	"	waterlily leaf beetle	water lily	F
Pyrrhalta					
perplexa (Fall.)	Coleoptera	Chrysomelidae	brown willow leaf beetle	willow	C

SCIENTIFIC NAME	ORDER	FAMILY	COMMON NAME	MAIN HOST PLANT(S) OR INSECT TYPE	IMPORTANCE RATING
Pyrrhalta					
spiraeae (Fall.)	Coleoptera	Chrysomelidae	meadowsweet leaf beetle	meadow sweet	F
tuberculata (Say)	"	"	willow leaf beetle	willow	C
Pyrrharctia (= *Isia*)					
isabella (J.E. Smith)	Lepidoptera	Arctiidae	banded woolly bear	ground plants	F
Pyrrhia					
exprimens (Wlk.)	Lepidoptera	Noctuidae	variable caterpillar	deciduous	B
umbra (Hufn.)	"	"	rose budworm	rose	C
Raphia					
frater Grt.	Lepidoptera	Noctuidae	yellowmarked caterpillar	aspen	C
Resseliella spp.	Diptera	Cecidomyiidae	midge	coniferous	B
Reticulitermes					
flavipes (Kol.)	Isoptera	Rhinotermitidae	eastern subterranean termite	dry wood	F
Rhabdophaga					
aceris (Shimer)	Diptera	Cecidomyiidae	soft maple leaf midge	soft maple	C
normaniana Felt	"	"	willow cabbagegall midge	willow	C
plicata Felt	"	"	willow gall midge	"	C
rosacea Felt	"	"	rosette midge	rose	C
salicis (Schr.)	"	"	willow twig-gall midge, or willow basket gall midge	willow	C
salicisbatatas (O. S.) (= *batatas* Walsh)	"	"	willow potatogall midge	"	C
salicisbrassicoides Pack.	"	"	willow cabbagegall midge	"	C
salicisnodulus (O.S.)	"	"	willow nodulegall midge	"	C
strobiloides (O.S.)	"	"	willow pinecone gall midge	"	C
swainei Felt	"	"	spruce bud midge	spruce	C

SCIENTIFIC NAME	ORDER	FAMILY	COMMON NAME	MAIN HOST PLANT(S) OR INSECT TYPE	IMPORTANCE RATING
Rhagium					
inquisitor (L.)	Coleoptera	Cerambycidae	longhorned beetle	deadwood	F
Rheumaptera					
hastata (L.)	Lepidoptera	Geometridae	spearmarked black moth	birch, alder, etc.	B
subhastata (Nolcken)	"	"	"	"	C
Rhopobota					
finitimana (Heinr.)	Lepidoptera	Olethreutinae	micro moth	ground plant	F
Rhyacionia					
adana Heinr.	Lepidoptera	Olethreutinae	pine tip moth	pine	B
buoliana (D. & S.)	"	"	European pine shoot moth	"	A
busckana Heinr.	"	"	red pine shoot borer	red, Scots pine	C
granti Miller	"	"	red jack pine shoot borer	jack pine, red pine	C
rigidana (Fern.)	"	"	pitch pine tip moth	pitch pine	E
sonia Miller	"	"	yellow jack pine shoot borer	jack pine	C
Rhynchaenus					
canus Horn	Coleoptera	Curculionidae	birch flea weevil	birch	C
ephippiatus Say	"	"	poplar flea weevil	poplar, willow	C
pallidior (Leng)	"	"	alder flea weevil	alder	C
rufipes (LeC.)	"	"	willow flea weevil	willow	C
subhirtus Horn	"	"	poplar flea weevil	poplar	C
uniformis (Brown)	"	"	serviceberry flea weevil	serviceberry	C
Salebriaria					
engeli (Dyar)	Lepidoptera	Pyralidae	oak leaftier	oak	C
Saperda					
calcarata Say	Coleoptera	Cerambycidae	poplar borer	poplar	C
candida F.	"	"	roundheaded appletree borer	apple tree	C
(inornata Say) see *Mecas*					
obliqua Say	"	"	alder stem borer	alder	C
tridentata Oliv.	"	"	elm borer	elm	C
vestita Say	"	"	linden borer	basswood	C

SCIENTIFIC NAME	ORDER	FAMILY	COMMON NAME	MAIN HOST PLANT(S) OR INSECT TYPE	IMPORTANCE RATING
Sarcophaga aldrichi Park.	Diptera	Sarcophagidae	parasite	parasite	D
Satyrium					
calanus falacer (Godt.)	Lepidoptera	Lycaenidae	banded hairstreak	oak, walnut	C
caryaevorum (McD.)	"	"	hickory hairstreak	hickory	C
liparops strigosum (Harr.)	"	"	striped hairstreak	deciduous	C
Saucrobotys futilalis (Led.)	Lepidoptera	Pyralidae	dogbane micro moth	dogbane	C
Schizolachnus piniradiatae (Dav.)	Homoptera	Aphididae	woolly pine needle aphid	red pine	C
Schizura					
concinna (J.E. Smith)	Lepidoptera	Notodontidae	redhumped caterpillar	deciduous	C
ipomoeae Dbldy.	"	"	oak-maple humped caterpillar	"	C
leptinoides (Grt.)	"	"	humped caterpillar	"	C
semirufescens Wlk.	"	"	"	"	C
unicornis (J.E. Smith)	"	"	unicorn caterpillar	"	C
Schreckensteinia erythriella (Clem.)	Lepidoptera	Heliodinidae	sumac micro moth	sumac	C
Sciaphilus asperatus Bonsd.	Coleoptera	Curculionidae	weevil	unknown	C
Scirtes					
orbiculatus F.	Coleoptera	Helodidae	marsh beetle	unknown	C
tibialis Guér.	"	"	"	"	C
Scolioneura betuleti Klug.	Hymenoptera	Tenthredinidae	birch edgeminer	European birch	C
Scoliopteryx libatrix (L.)	Lepidoptera	Noctuidae	herald moth	willow	C

SCIENTIFIC NAME	ORDER	FAMILY	COMMON NAME	MAIN HOST PLANT(S) OR INSECT TYPE	IMPORTANCE RATING
Scolytus					
mali (Bechst.)	Coleoptera	Scolytidae	larger shothole borer	bark beetle	C
multistriatus (Marsh.)	"	"	smaller European elm bark beetle	elm	A
piceae (Swaine)	"	"	spruce bark beetle	spruce	C
quadrispinosus Say	"	"	hickory bark beetle	hickory	C
rugulosus (Müll.)	"	"	shothole borer	fruit trees	C
Scythropus					
elegans Couper	Coleoptera	Curculionidae	elegant pine weevil	pine	C
Selenia					
alciphearia Wlk.	Lepidoptera	Geometridae	looper	deciduous	C
Semanotus					
ligneus (F.)	Coleoptera	Cerambycidae	cedartree borer	cedar, juniper	C
Semioscopis					
aurorella Dyar	Lepidoptera	Oecophoridae	micro moth	cherry	C
inornata Wlsm.	"	"	poplar micro moth	poplar	C
Semiothisa					
aemulataria (Wlk.)	Lepidoptera	Geometridae	deciduous tree looper	deciduous	C
banksianae Fgn.	"	"	jack pine looper	jack pine	C
bicolorata (F.)	"	"	"	hard pines	C
bisignata (Wlk.)	"	"	white pine looper	white pine	C
fissinotata (Wlk.)	"	"	lesser hemlock looper	hemlock	C
mellistrigata (Grt.)	"	"	willow looper	willow	C
minorata (Pack.)	"	"	white pine looper	pine	C
neptaria (Gn.)	"	"	willow-poplar looper	willow, poplar	C
ocellinata (Gn.)	"	"	locust looper	locust	C
orillata (Wlk.)	"	"	cedar looper	cedar	C
oweni (Swett)	"	"	Owen's larch looper	larch	C
pinistrobata Fgn.	"	"	white pine looper	white pine	C
sexmaculata (Pack.)	"	"	green larch looper	larch	C
signaria dispuncta (Wlk.)	"	"	spruce-fir looper	coniferous	C

SCIENTIFIC NAME	ORDER	FAMILY	COMMON NAME	MAIN HOST PLANT(S) OR INSECT TYPE	IMPORTANCE RATING
Semiothisa					
submarmorata (Wlk.)	Lepidoptera	Geometridae	larch looper	larch	C
transitaria (Wlk.)	"	"	pine looper	jack pine, red pine	C
ulsterata (Pears.)	"	"	deciduous tree looper	deciduous	C
Sereda					
tautana (Clem.)	Lepidoptera	Olethreutinae	micro moth	oak	C
Serica					
atricapilla Kby.	Coleoptera	Scarabaeidae	scarab beetle	deciduous	C
sericea Ill.	"	"	"	"	C
tristis LeC.	"	"	small leaf chafer	"	C
vespertina (Gyll.)	"	"	scarab beetle	"	C
Sericothrips					
tiliae Hood	Thysanoptera	Thripidae	basswood thrips	basswood	C
Sesia (= Aegeria)					
tibialis (Harr.)	Lepidoptera	Sesiidae	cottonwood crown borer	poplar	C
Setoptus					
jonesi (Keifer)	Acari	Eriophyidae	red pine needle mite	red pine	C
strobacus Keifer	"	"	pine needle mite	white and red pine	C
Sialis					
infumata Newn.	Neuroptera	Sialidae	alderfly	aquatic insect	F
Sicya					
macularia (Harr.)	Lepidoptera	Geometridae	twopronged looper	deciduous	C
Sideridis					
rosea (Harv.)	Lepidoptera	Noctuidae	owlet moth	deciduous	C
Simulium					
venustum Say	Diptera	Simuliidae	whitestockinged black fly	biting insect	F
Simyra					
henrici (Grt.)	Lepidoptera	Noctuidae	owlet moth	ground plants	C

SCIENTIFIC NAME	ORDER	FAMILY	COMMON NAME	MAIN HOST PLANT(S) OR INSECT TYPE	IMPORTANCE RATING
Sinea *diadema* (Fab.)	Hemiptera	Reduviidae	spined assassin bug	predator	D
Sinoe *robiniella* (Fitch)	Lepidoptera	Gelechiidae	locust leaftier	locust	C
Smerinthus *cerisyi* Kby.	Lepidoptera	Sphingidae	poplar-and-willow hornworm	poplar, willow	C
jamaicensis (Drury)	"	"	twin-spot sphinx	willow, poplar	C
Solenobia *walshella* Clem.	Lepidoptera	Psychidae	bagworm	coniferous	C
Somatochlora spp.	Odonata	Libellulidae	dragon fly	predator	D
Spaelotis *clandestina* (Harr.)	Lepidoptera	Noctuidae	w-marked cutworm	general feeder	C
Spargania *luctuata obductata* (Mösch.)	Lepidoptera	Geometridae	looper	unknown	C
magnoliata Gn.	"	"	"	white spruce	C
Sparganothis *acerivorana* MacK.	Lepidoptera	Tortricidae	maple leafroller	maple	C
diluticostana (Wlsm.)	"	"	leafroller	unknown	C
directana (Wlk.)	"	"	chokecherry leafroller	chokecherry	C
flavibasana (Fern.)	"	"	leafroller	ground plants	F
niveana (Wlsm.)	"	"	"	ironwood, maple	C
pettitana (Rob.)	"	"	maple-basswood leafroller	basswood, maple	C
reticulatana (Clem.)	"	"	leafroller	deciduous	C
sulfureana (Clem.)	"	"	needletier	general feeder	C
tristriata Kft.	"	"	"	"	C
umbrana B. & Bsk.	"	"	"	basswood	C
unifasciana (Clem.)	"	"	"	pine, spruce	C

SCIENTIFIC NAME	ORDER	FAMILY	COMMON NAME	MAIN HOST PLANT(S) OR INSECT TYPE	IMPORTANCE RATING
Speyeria					
aphrodite (F.)	Lepidoptera	Nymphalidae	aphrodite	violets	F
cybele (F.)	"	"	great spangled fritillary	"	F
Sphinx					
canadensis Bdv.	Lepidoptera	Sphingidae	northern ash sphinx	ash	C
chersis (Hbn.)	"	"	great ash sphinx	deciduous	C
drupiferarum J.E. Smith	"	"	wild-cherry sphinx	fruit trees	C
gordius Cram.	"	"	apple sphinx	larch, apple	C
kalmiae J.E. Smith	"	"	laurel sphinx	deciduous	C
luscitiosa Clem.	"	"	poplar-and-willow sphinx, or Clemen's hawkmoth	poplar, willow, birch	C
Spilonota					
ocellana (D. & S.)	Lepidoptera	Olethreutinae	eyespotted bud moth	fruit trees, larch	C
Spilosoma (= *Estigmene* in part)					
dubia (Wlk.) (= *prima* Slosson)	Lepidoptera	Arctiidae	woollybear	grasses	F
virginica (F.)	"	"	yellow woollybear	deciduous	C
(*Stenoma*) see *Antaeotricha*					
Sterictiphora					
sericea (Nort.)	Hymenoptera	Argidae	hawthorn sawfly	hawthorn	C
(*Sternochetus*) see *Cryptorhynchus*					
Sthenopis					
argenteomaculatus (Harr.)	Lepidoptera	Hepialidae	alder rootborer	alder	C
purpurascens (Pack.)	"	"	rootborer	roots	C
quadriguttatus (Grt.)	"	"	poplar-and-willow rootborer	poplar, willow	C

SCIENTIFIC NAME	ORDER	FAMILY	COMMON NAME	MAIN HOST PLANT(S) OR INSECT TYPE	IMPORTANCE RATING
Stigmella					
castaneaefoliella (Cham.)	Lepidoptera	Nepticulidae	chestnut leafminer	chestnut	C
latifasciella (Cham.) (= *macrocarpae* Free.)	"	"	oak serpentine leaf-miner	oak	C
Stilbosis					
ostryaeella (Cham.)	Lepidoptera	Cosmopterygidae	ironwood leafminer	ironwood	C
(Stilpnotia) see *Leucoma*					
Stretchia					
plusiaeformis Hy. Edw.	Lepidoptera	Noctuidae	owlet moth	currant	F
Strictoleptura					
canadensis Oliv.	Coleoptera	Cerambycidae	redshouldered pine borer	coniferous	C
Strongylogaster					
multicincta Nort.	Hymenoptera	Tenthredinidae	sawfly	bracken	F
Sunira					
bicolorago (Gn.)	Lepidoptera	Noctuidae	owlet moth	ground plants, and possibly tree seeds	F
Swammerdamia					
caesiella (Hbn.)	Lepidoptera	Yponomeutidae	birch micro moth	birch	C
pyrella (Villers)	"	"	cherry micro moth	cherry	C
Symmerista					
canicosta Franc.	Lepidoptera	Notodontidae	redhumped oakworm	oak	C
leucitys Franc.	"	"	orangehumped mapleworm	maple	C
Symydobius (= *Neosymydobius*)					
americanus Baker	Homoptera	Aphididae	dark birch aphid	birch	C
Synanthedon					
acerni (Clem.)	Lepidoptera	Sesiidae	maple callus borer	maple	C
bolteri (Hy. Edw.)	"	"	willow borer	willow	C

SCIENTIFIC NAME	ORDER	FAMILY	COMMON NAME	MAIN HOST PLANT(S) OR INSECT TYPE	IMPORTANCE RATING
Synanthedon					
exitiosa (Say)	Lepidoptera	Sesiidae	peachtree borer	fruit trees	C
pictipes (G. & R.)	"	"	lesser peachtree borer	deciduous	C
pini (Kell.)	"	"	pitch mass borer	pine, spruce	C
tipuliformis (Clerck)	"	"	currant borer	currant	C
viburni Engelh.	"	"	viburnum borer	viburnum	C
Syndemis					
afflictana (Wlk.)	Lepidoptera	Tortricidae	micro moth	general feeder	C
Synchlora					
aerata (F.)	Lepidoptera	Geometridae	camouflaged looper	sweetfern, birch	F
Syneta					
ferruginea (Germ.)	Coleoptera	Chrysomelidae	rusty leaf beetle	deciduous	C
Syngrapha					
alias (Ottol.)	Lepidoptera	Noctuidae	spruce climbing cutworm	coniferous	C
epigaea (Grt.)	"	"	blueberry false looper	blueberry	F
octoscripta (Grt.)	"	"	false looper	unknown	C
rectangula (Kby.)	"	"	balsam fir false looper	coniferous	C
selecta (Wlk.)	"	"	spruce false looper	"	C
Syrphus					
rectus O.S.	Diptera	Syrphidae	hover fly	predator	D
Tacparia					
detersata (Gn.)	Lepidoptera	Geometridae	leaping looper	alder	C
Taenioglyptes					
fraseri (Hopk.)	Coleoptera	Scolytidae	bark beetle	white spruce	C
(*Taniva*) see *Endothenia*					
Tarachidia					
candefacta (Hbn.)	Lepidoptera	Noctuidae	ragweed false looper	ragweed	F
erastriodes (Gn.)	"	"	"	"	F

SCIENTIFIC NAME	ORDER	FAMILY	COMMON NAME	MAIN HOST PLANT(S) OR INSECT TYPE	IMPORTANCE RATING
Telamona					
tiliae Ball	Homoptera	Membracidae	treehopper	deciduous	C
tremulata Ball	"	"	aspen treehopper	aspen	C
Telphusa, (see also *Pseudotelphusa* and *Neotelphusa*)					
longifasciella (Clem.)	Lepidoptera	Gelechiidae	sumac micro moth	sumac	C
Tethida					
cordigera (Beauv.)	Hymenoptera	Tenthredinidae	blackheaded ash sawfly	ash	C
Tetracis					
cachexiata Gn.	Lepidoptera	Geometridae	looper	general feeder	C
crocallata Gn.	"	"	"	willow	C
Tetralopha					
aplastella (Hlst.)	Lepidoptera	Pyralidae	aspen webworm	aspen, birch	C
asperatella (Clem.)	"	"	maple webworm	maple	C
expandens (Wlk.)	"	"	striped oak webworm	oak	C
maritimalis McD.	"	"	larch webworm	larch, spruce	C
militella Zell.	"	"	sycamore webworm	sycamore	C
robustella Zell.	"	"	pine webworm	pine	C
vaccinivora Mun.	"	"	blueberry webworm	blueberry	C
Tetropium					
cinnamopterum Kby.	Coleoptera	Cerambycidae	eastern larch borer	spruce, pine	C
Tetyra					
bipunctata (H.-S.)	Hemiptera	Pentatomidae	shieldbacked pine seedbug	pine seed	C
Thanasimus					
dubius F.	Coleoptera	Cleridae	checkered beetle	predator	D
Thecabuius					
affinis (Kalt.)	Homoptera	Aphididae	purse leaf gall aphid	poplar	C

SCIENTIFIC NAME	ORDER	FAMILY	COMMON NAME	MAIN HOST PLANT(S) OR INSECT TYPE	IMPORTANCE RATING
Thecodiplosis					
liriodendri (O.S.)	Diptera	Cecidomyiidae	tulip spotgall midge	tulip, poplar	C
piniresinosae Kearby	"	"	red pine needle midge	red pine	C
Thera					
contractata (Pack.)	Lepidoptera	Geometridae	juniper looper	juniper	C
juniperata L.	"	"	"	"	C
Thymelicus					
lineola (Ochs.)	Lepidoptera	Hesperiidae	European skipper	timothy	G
Thyridopteryx					
ephemeraeformis (Haw.)	Lepidoptera	Psychidae	bagworm	coniferous	C
Tibicen					
canicularis Harr.	Homoptera	Cicadidae	cicada	larva in soil	C
Tischeria					
castaneaeella Cham. (prob. not Ontario)	Lepidoptera	Tischeriidae	oak leafminer	oak	C
citrinipennella Clem.	"	"	oakleaf edgeminer	oak, chestnut	C
malifoliella Clem.	"	"	appleleaf trumpet-miner	fruit trees	C
Tlascala					
reductella (Wlk.)	Lepidoptera	Pyralidae	locust leaftier	black locust	C
Tolype					
laricis (Fitch)	Lepidoptera	Lasiocampidae	larch lappet moth	coniferous	C
velleda (Stoll)	"	"	vellada lappet moth	deciduous	C
Tomostethus					
multicinctus (Roh.)	Hymenoptera	Tenthredinidae	brownheaded ash sawfly	ash	C
Tortricidia					
flexuosa (Grt.)	Lepidoptera	Limacodidae	slug caterpillar	oak, maple	C
pallida (H.-S.)	"	"	"	beech, maple	C

(Tortrix) see *Aphelia*

SCIENTIFIC NAME	ORDER	FAMILY	COMMON NAME	MAIN HOST PLANT(S) OR INSECT TYPE	IMPORTANCE RATING
Toumeyella *parvicornis* (Ckll.) (= *numismaticum* [P.&M.])	Homoptera	Coccidae	pine tortoise scale	jack and Scots pine	B
(*Trachoma*) see *Ypsolopha*					
Trachysida *mutabilis* (Newn.)	Coleoptera	Cerambycidae	longhorn beetle	deciduous	C
Tremex *columba* (L.)	Hymenoptera	Siricidae	pigeon tremex	deciduous	C
Tribolium *castaneum* (Hbst.)	Coleoptera	Tenebrionidae	red flour beetle	household pest	G
confusum Duv.	"	"	confused flour beetle	"	G
Trichiocampus *gregarius* (Dyar)	Hymenoptera	Tenthredinidae	hairy poplar sawfly	poplar	C
simplicicornis (Nort.) (= *irregularis* [Dyar])	"	"	hairy willow sawfly	willow	C
viminalis (Fall.)	"	"	hairy poplar sawfly	poplar, willow	C
Trichiosoma *triangulum* Kby.	Hymenoptera	Cimbicidae	giant birch sawfly	alder, ash, birch, *Prunus*, poplar, willow	C
Trichiotinus *affinis* (G. & P.)	Coleoptera	Scarabaeidae	scarab beetle	ground plants	F
assimilis Kby.	"	"	"	"	F
Trichogramma *minutum* Riley	Hymenoptera	Trichogrammat- idae	minute egg parasite	Lepidoptera eggs	D
Trichoplusia *ni* (Hbn.)	Lepidoptera	Noctuidae	cabbage looper	cabbage, flowers	F

SCIENTIFIC NAME	ORDER	FAMILY	COMMON NAME	MAIN HOST PLANT(S) OR INSECT TYPE	IMPORTANCE RATING
Trichoptilus lobidactylus (Fitch)	Lepidoptera	Pterophoridae	plume moth	goldenrod	F
Trichotaphe levisella Fyles	Lepidoptera	Gelechiidae	aster micro moth	aster	F
setosella Clem.	"	"	micro moth	cedar, pine	C
Trigonarthis minnesotana Casey	Coleoptera	Cerambycidae	Minnesota longhorn beetle	deciduous	C
proximis (Say)	"	"	longhorn beetle	gum tree	C
Trisetacus alborum Keif.	Acari	Eriophyidae	white pine needle mite	white pine	C
ehamanni Keif.	"	"	jack pine needle-sheath mite	jack pine	C
grosmanni Keif.	"	"	fir bud mite	balsam fir, spruce, red pine	C
Trishormomya canadensis (Felt)	Diptera	Cecidomyiidae	juneberry lippedgall midge	serviceberry	C
crataegifolia (Felt)	"	"	coxcombgall midge	hawthorn	C
salicisverruca (O. S.)	"	"	willow lippedgall midge	willow	C
Trypodendron betulae Sw.	Coleoptera	Scolytidae	birch ambrosia beetle	birch	C
lineatum (Oliv.)	"	"	striped ambrosia beetle	coniferous	C
retusum (LeC.)	"	"	poplar ambrosia beetle	poplar	C
rufitarsis (Kby.)	"	"	conifer ambrosia beetle	spruce, pine	C
Tuberolachnus salignus (Gmel.)	Homoptera	Aphididae	giant willow aphid	willow	C
Typocerus velutinus (Oliv.)	Coleoptera	Cerambycidae	longhorned beetle	dead wood	C

SCIENTIFIC NAME	ORDER	FAMILY	COMMON NAME	MAIN HOST PLANT(S) OR INSECT TYPE	IMPORTANCE RATING
Upis					
ceramboides (L.)	Coleoptera	Tenebrionidae	roughened darkling beetle	deciduous	C
Urocerus					
albicornis (F.)	Hymenoptera	Siricidae	whitehorned horntail	coniferous	C
gigas flavicornis (F.)	"	"	yellowhorned horntail	"	C
Valentinia					
glandulella (Riley)	Lepidoptera	Blasotbasidae	acorn moth	oak	C
Vanessa (see also *Cynthia*)					
atalanta (L.)	Lepidoptera	Nymphalidae	red admiral	nettles	F
cardui (L.)	"	"	painted lady	thistle	F
virginiensis (Drury)	"	"	painted beauty	flowers	F
Vasates					
aceris-crumena (Riley)	Acari	Eriophyidae	maple spindlegall mite	maple	C
quadripedes Shimer	"	"	maple bladdergall mite	"	C
Venusia					
cambrica Curt.	Lepidoptera	Geometridae	alder looper	alder	C
comptaria (Wlk.)	"	"	"	"	C
(*Vespamima*) see *Synanthedon*					
Vespula					
arenaria (F.)	Hymenoptera	Vespidae	yellowjacket	predator	D
maculata (L.)	"	"	baldfaced hornet, or whitefaced hornet	"	D
Winnertzia					
hudsonici Felt	Diptera	Cecidomyiidae	fringed cupgall midge	hawthorn	C
Xanthia					
togata (Esp.) (= *lutea* (Ström)	Lepidoptera	Noctuidae	pinkbarred sallow	deciduous	C

SCIENTIFIC NAME	ORDER	FAMILY	COMMON NAME	MAIN HOST PLANT(S) OR INSECT TYPE	IMPORTANCE RATING
Xanthonia decemnotata (Say)	Coleoptera	Chrysomelidae	tenspotted leaf beetle	birch, hazel	C
Xanthoteras quercusforticorne (Walsh) (= *forticorne* [O.S.])	Hymenoptera	Cynipidae	oak fig-gall wasp	oak	C
Xanthotype sospeta (Drury)	Lepidoptera	Geometridae	crocus geometer	deciduous	C
urticaria Swett	"	"	"	maple	C
Xenotemna (= *Aphelia* in part) *pallorana* (Rob.)	Lepidoptera	Tortricidae	pine-and-clover tier	pine, clover	C
Xerophylla (= *Phylloxera*) *caryaecaulis* (Fitch)	Homoptera	Adelgidae	hickory gall adelgid	hickory	C
caryaeglobuli (Walsh)	"	"	globular hickory gall adelgid	"	C
foveola (Perg.)	"	"	hickory buttongall adelgid	"	C
vitifoliae (Fitch)	"	"	grape adelgid	grape, hickory?	C
Xestia (= *Amathes*) *adela* Franc. (= *c-nigrum*, part)	Lepidoptera	Noctuidae	spotted cutworm	agricultural pest	F
dolosa Franc. (= *c-nigrum*, part)	"	"	"	"	F
normaniana (Grt.)	"	"	cutworm	plantain	C
smithii (Snell.)	"	"	"	general feeder	C
Xyela minor Nort.	Hymenoptera	Xyelidae	pine flower sawfly	pine flowers	C
Xylena cineritia (Grt.)	Lepidoptera	Noctuidae	swordgrass moth	deciduous	C
curvimacula (Morr.)	"	"	dot-and-dash swordgrass moth	"	C
nupera (Lint.)	"	"	red swordgrass moth	"	C
Xylococculus betulae (Perg.)	Homoptera	Coccidae	birch margarodid	birch	C

SCIENTIFIC NAME	ORDER	FAMILY	COMMON NAME	MAIN HOST PLANT(S) OR INSECT TYPE	IMPORTANCE RATING
(Xylomyges) see *Egira*					
Xylotrechus					
aceris Fisher	Coleoptera	Cerambycidae	gallmaking maple borer	maple	C
obliteratus LeC.	"	"	poplar butt borer	poplar	C
undulatus (Say)	"	"	spruce zebra beetle	coniferous	C
Yponomeuta					
cagnagella Hbn.	Lepidoptera	Yponomeutidae	euonymus moth	euonymus	C
(= *cognatella* Hbn., misspell.)					
multipunctella Clem.	"	"	" "	"	C
Ypsolopha (= *Trachoma*)					
falciferella (Wlsm.)	Lepidoptera	Plutellidae	fruittree leafroller	fruit trees	C
dentella F.	"	"	European honeysuckle leafroller	honeysuckle	C
Zale					
aeruginosa (Gn.)	Lepidoptera	Noctuidae	large false looper	jack pine	C
duplicata (Beth.)	"	"	pine zale	pine	C
duplicata largera (Sm.)	"	"	pine false looper	"	C
galbanata (Morr.)	"	"	maple false looper	maple	C
helata (Sm.)	"	"	white pine false looper	pine	C
horrida Hbn.	"	"	large false looper	unknown	C
lunifera (Hbn.)	"	"	pine false looper	pine	C
metatoides McD.	"	"	jack pine false looper	jack pine	C
minerea (Gn.)	"	"	large false looper	deciduous	C
minera norda (Sm.)	"	"	" "	"	C
obliqua (Gn.)	"	"	jack pine false looper	pine	C
squamularis (Drury)	"	"	large false looper	"	C
submediana Strand	"	"	pine false looper	"	C
undularis (Drury)	"	"	locust false looper	locust	C
unilineata (Grt.)	"	"	large false looper	unknown, prob. locust	C

SCIENTIFIC NAME	ORDER	FAMILY	COMMON NAME	MAIN HOST PLANT(S) OR INSECT TYPE	IMPORTANCE RATING
Zanclognatha					
cruralis (Gn.)	Lepidoptera	Noctuidae	owlet moth	unknown	C
jacchusalis (Wlk.)	"	"	"	"	C
laevigata (Grt.)	"	"	"	yellow birch	C
minoralis Sm.	"	"	"	spruce, balsam fir	C
protumnusalis (Wlk.)	"	"	"	coniferous	C
theralis (Wlk.)	"	"	"	unknown	C
Zaraea					
americana Cress.	Hymenoptera	Cimbicidae	sawfly	deciduous	C
inflata Nort.	"	"	honeysuckle sawfly	honeysuckle	C
Zeiraphera					
canadensis Mut. & Free. (= *ratzeburgiana* auth.)	Lepidoptera	Olethreutinae	spruce bud moth	spruce	B
fortunana (Kft.)	"	"	yellow spruce budworm	spruce	C
improbana (Wlk.) (= *diniana* auth.; *destitutana* [Wlk.])	"	"	larch needleworm	larch, spruce	C
unfortunana Powell	"	"	purplestriped shootworm	white spruce	C
Zelleria					
haimbachi Bsk.	Lepidoptera	Yponomeutidae	pine needle sheathminer	jack pine	C
Zelus					
audax Banks	Hemiptera	Reduviidae	assassin bug	predator	D
Zeugophora					
abnormis LeC.	Coleoptera	Chrysomelidae	poplar blackmine beetle	poplar	C
scutellaris Suffr.	"	"	cottonwood leafmining beetle	"	C
varians Crotch	"	"	poplar blackmine beetle	"	C

INDEX OF COMMON NAMES

SELECTED BIBLIOGRAPHY

ARNETT, R.H. Jr. 1963. The beetles of the United States (A manual for identification). The Catholic Univ. of Amer. Press, Wash., D.C. 1112 p.

BAKER, W.L. 1972. Eastern forest insects. USDA For. Serv., Misc. Publ. No. 1175. 642 p.

BELTON, E.M., *Ed.* and *Comp.* 1985. English common names of insects and other pests (preliminary, unpublished). Insect Common Names Committee, Ent. Soc. Can. 100 p.

BENOIT, P., *Ed.* and *Comp.* 1985. Nomenclatura insectorum canadensium. Que. Soc. Prot. Plants/Laurentian For. Centre, Can. For. Serv., Ste. Foy, Que. 214 p.

BORROR, D.J., DELONG, D.M. and TRIPLEHORN, C.A. 1976. An introduction to the study of insects. 4th ed. Holt, Rinehart and Winston, Toronto, Ont. 852. p.

BRIGHT, D.E. Jr. 1976. The insects and arachnids of Canada, Part 2. The bark beetles of Canada and Alaska. Biosystematics Res. Inst., Can. Dep. Agric., Ottawa, Ont. 241 p.

COVELL, C.V. Jr. 1984. A field guide to the moths of eastern North America. Houghton Mifflin Co., Boston, Mass. 496 p.

DAVIDSON, A.G., *Comp.* 1980. Insect catalogue. Forest Insect and Disease Survey. Dep. Environ., Can. For. Serv., Ottawa, Ont. Unpubl. Cat. 304 p.

DILLON, E.S. and DILLON, L.S. 1961. A manual of common beetles of eastern North America. Row, Peterson and Co., Evanston, Ill., Elmsford, N.Y. 884 p.

DOMINICK, R.B., DOMINICK, T., FERGUSON, D.C., FRANCLEMONT, J.G., HODGES, R.W. and MONROE, E.G., *Ed.* 1971. The moths of America north of Mexico including Greenland. E.W. Classey Ltd. and The Wedge Entomological Research Foundation, London, England. (13 fascicles to date).

DROOZE, A.T. 1985. Insects of eastern forests. USDA For. Serv., Misc. Publ. No. 1426. 608 p.

EASTOP, V.F. and HILLE RIS LAMBERS, D. 1976. Survey of the world's aphids. Dr. W. Junk b.v., The Hague. 573. p.

FELT, E.P. 1940. Plant galls and gall makers. Comstock Publ. Co. Inc., Ithaca, N.Y. 364 p.

FORBES, W.T.M. 1923. The Lepidoptera of New York and neighboring states. Cornell Univ. Agric. Exp. Stn., Mem. 68. 729 p.

FORBES, W.T.M.   1948.   Lepidoptera of New York and neighboring states. Part II.   Cornell Univ. Agric. Exp. Stn., Mem. 274.   263 p.

FORBES, W.T.M.   1954.   Lepidoptera of New York and neighboring states, Part III.   Cornell Univ. Agric. Exp. Stn., Mem. 329.   433 p.

FORBES, W.T.M.   1960.   Lepidoptera of New York and neighboring states, Part IV.   Cornell Univ. Agric. Exp. Stn., Mem. 371.   188 p.

HEDLIN, A.F., YATES, H.O. III, TOVAR, D.C., EBEL, B.H., KOERBER, T.W. and MERKEL, E.P.   1980.   Cone and seed insects of North American conifers.   Dep. Environ., Can. For. Serv., Ottawa, Ont.   122 p.

HODGES, R.W., DOMINICK, T., DAVIS, D.R., FERGUSON, D.C., FRANCLEMONT, J.G., MUNROE, E.G. and POWELL, J.A., *Ed*.   1983. Checklist of the lepidoptera of America north of Mexico including Greenland. E.W. Classey Ltd. and The Wedge Entomological Research Foundation, London, England.

HOLLAND, W.J.   1968.   The moth book.   Dover Publ. Inc., New York, N.Y. 479 p.

HOWE, W.H., *Ed*.   1975.   The butterflies of North America.   Doubleday and Co. Inc., Garden City, N.Y.   633 p.

KLOTS, A.B.   1951.   A field guide to the butterflies of North America, east of the Great Plains.   Houghton Mifflin Co., Boston, Mass. 349 p.

KROMBEIN, K.V., HURD, P.D. Jr., SMITH, D.R. and BURKS, B.D.   1979. Catalog of hymenoptera in America north of Mexico, Smithsonian Inst. Press, Washington, D.C.   3 vol. 2735 p.

LENG, C.W.   1920.   Catalogue of the coleoptera of America, north of Mexico.   The Cosmos Press, Cambridge, Mass.   470 p.

LUTZ, F.E.   1935.   Field book of insects.   G.P. Putman's Sons, New York. 510 p.

McALPINE, J.F., PETERSON, B.V., SHEWELL, G.E., TESKEY, H.J., VOCKEROTH, J.R. and WOOD, D.M.   1981.   Manual of nearctic diptera, Vol. 1, Res. Br., Agric. Can. Mon. No. 27.   674 p.

McGUGAN, B.M., *Comp*.   1958.   Forest lepidoptera of Canada, Vol. I.   Dep. Agric., For. Biol. Div., Ottawa, Ont., Publ. 1034.   76 p.

O'BRIEN, C.W. and WIBMER, C.J.   1982.   Annotated checklest of the weevils (Curculionidae *sensu lato)* of North America, Central America and the West Indies (Coleoptera: Curculionidae).   Mem. Am. Ent. Inst. No. 34.   382 p.

PRENTICE, R.M., *Comp*.   1962.   Forest lepidoptera of Canada, Vol. 2. Gov't of Can., Dep. For., Bull. 128.   p. 77-281.

PRENTICE, R.M., *Comp.* 1963. Forest lepidoptera of Canada, Vol. 3. Gov't of Can., Dep. For., Publ. 1013. p. 282-543.

PRENTICE, R.M., *Comp.* 1965. Forest lepidoptera of Canada, Vol. 4. Gov't of Can., Dep. For., Publ. 1142. p. 544-840.

ROSE, A.H. and LINDQUIST, O.H. 1980. Insects of eastern larch, cedar and juniper. Dep. Environ., Can. For. Serv., Ottawa, Ont., For. Tech. Rep. 28. 100 p.

ROSE, A.H. and LINDQUIST, O.H. 1982. Insects of eastern hardwood trees. Dep. Environ., Can. For. Serv., Ottawa, Ont., For. Tech. Rep. 29. 304 p.

ROSE, A.H. and LINDQUIST, O.H. 1984. Insects of eastern pines. 2nd ed. Dep. Environ., Can. For. Serv., Ottawa, Ont., Publ. 1313. 127 p.

ROSE, A.H. and LINDQUIST, O.H. 1985. Insects of eastern spruces, fir and hemlock. 2nd ed. Dep. Environ., Can. For. Serv., Ottawa, Ont. For.Tech. Rep. 23. 159 p.

STONE, A., SABROSKY, C.W., WIRTH, W.W., FOOTE, R.H. and COULSON, J.R. 1965. A catalog of the diptera of America north of Mexico. USDA, Agric. Handb. No. 276. 1696 p.

TITUS, F.A., MEIKLE, O.A. and HARRISON, K.J. 1985. Scientific and common names of insects and mites of interest in the Maritime Provinces. Gov't of Can., Can. For. Serv., Fredericton, N.B. Inf. Rep. M-X-155. 130 p.

WERNER, F.G., *Chairman.* 1982. Common names of insects and related organisms 1982. Ent. Soc. Am., Comm. on Common Names of Insects. 132 p.

Date Due

FEB 0 3 1997			

BRODART, INC.   Cat. No. 23 233   Printed in U.S.A.